A START
IN SMALLHOLDING

A START
IN SMALLHOLDING

by
Alan Beat

Foreword by Katie Thear

Smallholding Press

First published in the UK in 2004 by
Smallholding Press

ISBN 0-9546923-0-6

Printed by: Hedgerow Print, 16 Marsh Lane, Lords Meadow, Crediton, Devon EX17 1ES

Paper: Cyclus Offset, 100% recycled and non-chlorine bleached.

Further copies available from:
Smallholding Press,
The Bridge Mill,
Bridgerule,
Holsworthy,
Devon EX22 7EL

Cheques payable to Alan Beat for £6.00 plus £1 p & p per copy for UK mainland delivery; for all overseas delivery add £2.50 p&p per copy.

Contents

Foreword by Katie Thear 7

Acknowledgements 8

Introduction 9

Chapter 1   The beginning 12
First impressions of The Bridge Mill

Chapter 2   The reality 18

Chapter 3   Blooming ragwort 23

Chapter 4   Hens, ducks and vegetables 27

Chapter 5   The flood 32

Chapter 6   New skills on the land 36

Chapter 7   Banks, hedges and trees 40

Chapter 8   Machinery 44

Chapter 9   Building 46

Chapter 10   Starting with pigs 51

Chapter 11   Pork and bacon 57

Chapter 12   Watch out for mink 62

Chapter 13   Building the sheep flock 66

Chapter 14   Sheep skills 71

Chapter 15   An experience with orf 76

Chapter 16   Visitors 80

Chapter 17   Minimum dig vegetables 83

Chapter 18   The fox and the ducks 87

Chapter 19   Tea with lambs 90

Chapter 20   Lesson from the past 93

Chapter 21   Open to the public 96

Chapter 22   Looking back 100

Epilogue   106

Foreword

It gives me great pleasure to write the foreword to this book. I have known Alan and Rosie Beat for 13 years. It was in 1990 that Alan first sent me an article for publication in *Home Farm* magazine. Entitled *Tales of the Riverbank: Part I*, it immediately caught my attention because it was obviously an account of real experience. It described how the couple had moved from the town to live on a 16-acre smallholding in Devon. Unlike so many articles that I received and rejected at that time (because of a 'rose-tinted glasses' way of writing about rural themes) this one stood out! We could recognise its validity in relation to our own experiences as smallholders who had made a similar move in 1975. One paragraph in particular indicated that here was someone who did not shy away from reality:

"The reality is that we now work very much harder than before for very little monetary return, and that if we had relied on luck, we would never have made it here in the first place."

Many people have tried and failed when making such a move, but the Beats have made a success of it because they had a clear plan of what they wanted to do. They prepared for a number of years, ensuring that they could generate enough income from the sale of their home and business before moving. They also made certain that they had an outside income as they adapted and developed their smallholding. Each development and new enterprise was described in their articles, and proved very popular with readers. They detailed the problems that they encountered, as well as how these were overcome, aspects that people could relate to in their own experience.

The Beats are still writing for the magazine, now called *Country Smallholding*, and long may they continue to do so, but I welcome the decision to reprint the articles from those early years. Not only is the book a fascinating and rewarding story of a family that succeeded in making the move to the country, but it also acts as an inspiration and practical aid to those who seek to find a measure of self-sufficiency in their own lives.

Katie Thear.

Acknowledgements

I'd like to thank the many people who have helped me to find a better way of life in smallholding. Special thanks to Christine for choosing to sell the Bridge Mill to Rosie and I and for the friendship and encouragement she has given since; to Bill, for patiently passing on his farming knowledge to a raw novice and for being a true friend; to Katie Thear for accepting my early articles for publication in her magazine *Home Farm*; to Sara Priddle and Diane Cowgill, recent editors of the magazine, now *Country Smallholding*, for their continuing encouragement; and to Archant Devon, current owners of the magazine, for their co-operation.

Above all, thanks to Rosie, Katie and Martin - for everything.

Throughout this book, the original text of my "Home Farm" articles appears in Book Antiqua font.
Additional new material appears in Franklin Gothic Book font.

8

Introduction

Many people harbour the dream of escaping from an urban rat race and moving away to a country smallholding, where a slower pace of life beckons. With my wife Rosie and our two young children, I made that move in November 1987 after four years of planning. This book is our story.

I recorded our early experiences, as they happened, for *Home Farm* magazine (now re-named *Country Smallholding*) through a series of articles entitled *"Tales from the riverbank"*. Each article now forms the basis of a chapter in this book, with some additional new text for continuity. The temptation to modify and update this core material has been firmly resisted so that it retains, I sincerely hope, the fresh perspective of the novice that becomes so elusive in hindsight.

To set the scene to our story, readers may wish to know something about our background and the forces that drove us to make a complete change of lifestyle.

In our former lives Rosie was a primary school teacher, while I was a chartered mechanical engineer running a small family business. We married in 1974 to live in Aspley Guise on the Beds/Bucks border, close to the new city of Milton Keynes. We both had a love of the countryside and wildlife, Rosie through a special interest in plants, myself as a birdwatcher and keen angler - but we were nevertheless "townies" by birth and upbringing, with no family roots in farming.

Rosie's art and craft interests led her towards hand spinning. She bought a wheel; learned to spin and knit; joined the local guild of weavers, spinners and dyers; and began to dye wool using natural dyes. Selecting fleeces brought her into close proximity with sheep and their owners for the first time. She began growing dye plants in our own garden.

Meanwhile I was experiencing at first hand the environmental damage wrought by the Common Agricultural Policy as extensive land drainage, subsidised by public money, led to our rivers being dredged wider and straighter, to the great detriment of fish and all wildlife, so that the riverside meadows could be ploughed up to grow cereals that were already in surplus and had no market.

The birth of our daughter Katie in 1979 was a catalyst for change in our lives. She was a healthy baby while breast-fed, but developed infantile eczema as the weaning process introduced new foods to her. We read up on this condition to learn that the skin rash is often associated with cows milk products. Rosie confronted our doctor with this possibility, to which he replied that it was unlikely and that anyway, removing all cows milk products from her diet would be *"too much trouble"*.

He was wrong; nothing was too much trouble for Rosie where our precious baby was concerned. Within a short time she had established by experiment that feeding any derivatives of cows milk caused the eczema to flare up, while their removal allowed it to subside - and for the first time in our lives we started to examine the small print on food labels. This was a revelation to us, and we became concerned not only for what Katie was eating, but also for what we ourselves were eating.

A central part of Katie's new diet was goats milk from a local smallholding, where a retired naval officer and his wife kept a few tame animals. This was our first contact with such a lifestyle, and although we liked what we saw, there was no thought at that stage of doing anything similar.

We already made an effort to buy fresh, local produce, but now became aware of "organic" issues as well through a friend who introduced us to the Henry Doubleday Research Association (HDRA). Back then, it was impossible to buy organic food locally; the only answer was to grow your own. Rosie had dabbled at growing a few vegetables in previous years, while I had never even tried, but from that point onwards I gradually developed an interest, learning from the HDRA, from books and through the experience of a very small vegetable patch in our back garden.

Around this time I was becoming gradually disenchanted with my managerial role in the engineering business. This came to a head in 1983 when a major customer, an international company, suddenly closed its UK factory in breach of all previous assurances. This remote decision from the far side of the world removed one third of our sales turnover overnight, through no fault of our own; the effects of globalisation had shattered my illusion of independence. I made the decision that I would try to re-build the business back to a profitable turnover and then sell up. Perhaps we would buy a cottage in the country with a little land, grow our own organic food and keep a few sheep, while I would go fishing more often.

When I first outlined this to Rosie, her initial reaction was one of astonishment - but she quickly warmed to the idea! We began to talk it through, asking questions of ourselves. Where would we move? How would we earn our living? What were the implications for our children (we now had a second child, Martin, just a few months old)? At this stage we didn't have many answers, but the more we thought about it, the more determined we became to find them. We would move away from increasing traffic congestion, the sprawl of new building, a degraded environment, and employment that no longer appealed, to find an independent lifestyle in an unspoilt area of the country. This was where our future lay.

For the sake of the family business and those employed within it, we decided to say nothing of this to anyone else. I set about replacing the lost turnover, a long and difficult process that took three years to achieve. It took a further year to find a suitable buyer who would take on the company as a going concern; and during that final year, I began to develop the physical signs of stress-induced illness, the most visible being the gradual loss of all my hair – a condition that remains to this day as a permanent reminder of how ill I had become at that time.

Rosie had left her teaching post when Katie was first born, but looking ahead to the time when both children were themselves attending school, she was confident of finding supply or part-time work wherever we lived, should we need the income. I was already established in a small way as a freelance writer/photographer for angling magazines and newspapers, and this could be developed further when I had more time to both fish and write. These options provided a more confident background to our uncertain future income.

We set about answering as many of our questions as we could. We thought hard about where we might live, pored over weather maps of the UK and considered our past holiday experience. Important factors were the availability of good coarse fishing (for me) and a moderate climate, both of which ruled against the upland areas of Wales, Scotland and the North of England. We narrowed our search down to Dorset and Hampshire, and began taking holidays and short breaks in rural areas of these counties to look around. The housing market was booming, so we found that country properties with land were rocketing in price, while every sizeable outbuilding seemed to have planning permission for conversion into a dwelling, with a price tag to match, when we only wanted to keep a few sheep inside.

These factors pushed us gradually further west in our search for an affordable smallholding. I learned to accept the notion that good coarse fishing might not be locally available, but that this would be offset by new opportunities in sea and game fishing. We looked across Devon as far as the Cornish border . . . . . . but at this point, I must stand aside to allow the narrative of my first article for *Home Farm* to take up the story.

Chapter 1
The beginning

Two years ago we moved from the overcrowded Home Counties to begin a new life on a sixteen-acre smallholding in rural Devon. Now we keep sheep, hens, ducks and a pig, grow much of our own food, and lead an outdoor working life. To my former workmates, I had "retired"; to almost everyone, envious of our move, we were "lucky". The reality is that we now work very much harder than before for very little monetary return; and that if we had relied upon luck, we would never have made it here in the first place.

I appeared to be in a comfortable enough rut before, with well-paid employment, thirty-nine hour working week, company car, nice house, and one third of an acre of garden in a quiet village. But disillusion set in. More houses were built, more people lived in them, more cars carried them, the roads became more choked; the business I was involved with became more competitive, more stressful; people that I knew well suffered ill health, or even death, at an early age. Rosie and I had always loved the country, spending much of our leisure time in the open air. Gradually, the idea grew to 'escape' from a lifestyle that made less and less sense to us.

As with most people, our house was our most valuable asset. We had bought a sound but run-down 1930s house in what estate agents like to call a "sought after location". As our plans grew we put our available money and a lot of hard work towards upgrading it into a thoroughly saleable commodity. Looking around at other areas of the country and the house prices, we realised the possibility of selling up, buying outright a country cottage with a couple of acres of land and having some money left over to provide a modest investment income, not enough to live on by any means, but a useful amount which we could top-up from part-time working.

As we worked towards this, the price pattern changed. Our original target area, Dorset, went through the roof so we had to look further and further west, where prices remained lower. We wrote down a shopping list of priorities that we were looking for in both the property and the surrounding locality. This proved extremely useful and saved a lot of wasted time looking at places that failed one or more of our main criteria; the only trouble was that our list grew as we went on. One of the main difficulties we encountered was that any sizeable outbuilding or barn had planning permission for conversion to a dwelling - and we wanted such buildings for animals, quite apart from the obvious problems this presented of higher prices, immediate neighbours, shared access and so on.

The other main difficulty we encountered was estate agents. With rare exceptions, they were next to useless at matching our requirements with the properties on their books, supplying us with details that were clearly unsuitable, while overlooking others on their books that had possibilities. We found that the best way to overcome this was to visit the area in person, go round the agents, talk to them and make our own selection if any properties seemed worth a look, then follow up with phone calls, letters and more visits until they finally grasped that we were serious.

I did a good deal of the travelling and viewing on my own, as this was much easier and quicker than dragging wife plus two small children along too. The few properties that I short-listed they came to see on a return visit. I worked hard at finding the right place until, just as our spirits were flagging, I found it. I was alone but there was no doubting it. An auction was due in five weeks time, and with potential for development of the outbuildings it could well shoot out of our price range, so fast action was called for. I made an offer to purchase prior to auction, and this was accepted - before my wife had even seen the place! Of course I was on a safe wicket in this respect because Rosie and I were, and are, on the same wavelength - she loved it from the moment she saw it, and the children were excited too.

I will gloss over the difficulty of selling our own house, the horrendous bridging loan that we took on to bur our smallholding, the upheaval of moving away from family and friends for the first time in our lives. It was all worth it. At last we had arrived and could begin to put theory into practice.

We had been preparing for the new way of life for some time; around four years since the idea of changing it had become serious. Reading *Home Farm* magazine, and books by Patrick Rivers, Sedley Sweeny, John Seymour and other authors on self-sufficiency gave us a broadly based grounding upon which to build. Small-scale experience was gained in our own back garden with six laying hens, our very first livestock, while I began growing organic vegetables on what had once been the front lawn! We visited some farmers and smallholders that we knew socially, to learn from them, and visited some of the country shows and events that seemed appropriate.

Rosie was already an experienced hand spinner so sheep were very much on our agenda, and near to our moving date she attended a two-day introductory course on sheep breeding and general husbandry. All this preparation came in very useful, although with hindsight a few more short courses on my part would have been a wise investment. Not to worry, we had some idea to begin with and learned from there once we had actually started. Besides, all we had originally planned for was a couple of acres; how was I to know that we would end up with sixteen and a half that were run down and neglected to the point where every gateway, every hedge, every stonewall, every ditch needed full attention?

Footnote: To keep these first hens in our back garden, we bought a flat-packed hen house suitable for six layers, assembled it and built an outside run to go with it. The hens themselves were point-of-lay pullets (young birds just starting to lay) from a local outdoor flock. Once these had settled in to their new home, they were allowed access to a larger area of the garden under some trees where nothing much would grow, contained within a wire mesh fence. Here they scratched around happily and laid enough eggs to keep our kitchen supplied for most of the year except for the shortest winter months.

Our early attempts at growing vegetables were hampered by the position chosen – a small plot alongside a tall hedge. It was sunny enough, but the established hedge took most of the goodness from the soil to stunt the growth of crops grown close by. So a dramatic decision was made to dig up part of the front lawn instead. A trailer load of muck from a friendly farmer was tipped over the gate to feed this new vegetable bed, and the resulting crops improved considerably. So by the time we moved to our smallholding, we already had useful experience of keeping chickens and growing vegetables to start us off.

Rosie's two-day course on "starting with sheep" was not so useful in hindsight. It covered the minute details of lambing percentages, feeding efficiencies and profit margins, but little of relevance to students who just wanted to keep a few animals for their wool and meat. Many establishments that offer training courses in rural skills and small-scale farming are dependent upon commercial agriculture for their main income, and this may colour their approach to smaller-scale subjects (the Yarner Trust is different – see end pages for details).

First impressions of The Bridge Mill

I first encountered The Bridge Mill in September 1987 during a weekend of viewing potential properties. It lay on the east side of the village of Bridgerule, close to the border between Devon and Cornwall and within a few miles of the North Atlantic coast. The river Tamar formed a natural boundary to one side of the smallholding.

The cottage was thought to be over three hundred years old, built mainly of cob (earth mixed with chopped straw) on a stone base, with a slate roof replacing the original thatch. Grouped around the yard was a range of outbuildings that had once provided accommodation and feed storage for two heavy horses, six milking cows, a beef bullock and two fattening pigs.

The old corn mill had long since fallen into disuse. Entering this building was like stepping back in time. Some machinery and one pair of millstones remained in place, a few hand tools lay to one side, a bunch of string for tying flour sacks hung from a beam, a weights and measures notice from a bygone age was pinned to the wall. The miller might have stopped work yesterday, instead of fifty years ago.

Until that moment, I'd had no idea of ever owning, much less restoring, a water mill; but this was special. I looked around, asked questions, took in the atmosphere. The two waterwheels and some machinery were missing, the water no longer ran, there was some woodworm and rot in the timbers; but the building was basically sound with a good roof which, most importantly, had kept out the weather during the long years of disuse. I knew little about mills but with a background in engineering, I saw that the potential was there to set this mill working again - and the rest of the property was just what we had been looking for . . . . .

I outlined to the vendor that my intention would be to restore both the smallholding and the mill to working order again. I had no way of knowing that this was exactly what she wanted to hear. The estate agent had advised that the property be divided for sale as three lots based on the house, the stable and the mill, each with a few acres of land. Prospective buyers had enthused about the conversion potential of these outbuildings for holiday or residential use. Christine, the vendor, had listened politely but unknown to all, had her own private reasons for wanting The Bridge Mill to remain as one property.

We stepped innocently into this situation. Christine took us on trust, accepted our offer to purchase prior to auction, and soon became a close and valued friend along with her husband Alf.

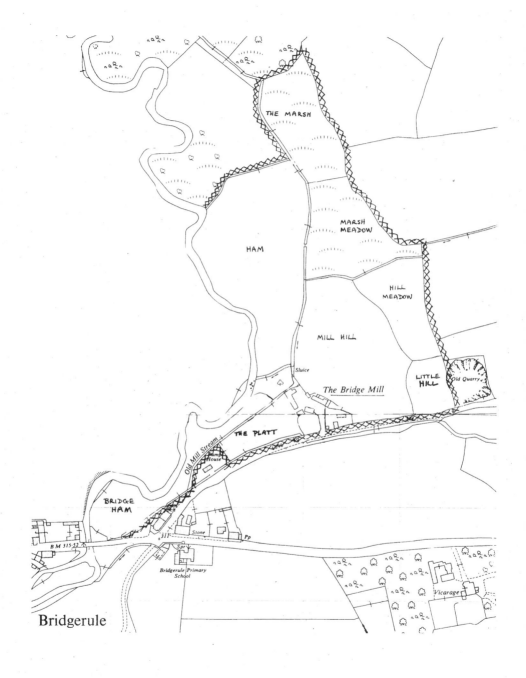

THE MARSH

MARSH MEADOW

HAM

HILL MEADOW

MILL HILL

Sluice

The Bridge Mill

LITTLE HILL

Old Quarry

THE PLATT

Old Mill Stream

Mill House

BRIDGE HAM

B M 315·52

311

Stone

Pp

Spr

Bridgerule Primary School

Vicarage

Bridgerule

17

Chapter 2
The reality

After a lifetime of living with a house-and-garden, the culture shock of moving to a smallholding comprising farmhouse, range of outbuildings and sixteen and a half acres of land was enormous. Following all the planning and preparation, our hopes and dreams were suddenly reality; we had arrived!

The house had been rented out to an elderly couple for the past fourteen years and was rather run-down, but the former owner went to some considerable trouble to prepare the place for our arrival. We found fresh paint where badly needed, a spring clean throughout, the solid fuel range alight and warming pasties not only for ourselves but the removal men as well. It was a much-appreciated first taste of Devon hospitality.

The electrical circuits were dubious to say the least, with round-pin five amp sockets and ancient rubber-sheathed cable that powdered to the touch. There was one solitary thirteen amp modern socket in the kitchen, where the previous tenant had plugged in his electric cooker. *"But don't switch on the hob at the same time as the oven"* he solemnly warned *"or the fuse will blow"*. We cooked on the range and used this socket for all our power appliances, using only low-power devices elsewhere to manage for the time being.

The plumbing was primitive but seemed to work. The kitchen contained an old "Belfast" sink with hot and cold taps, a clip-on draining board and one shelf on the wall - nothing else! The low doorways took some getting used to; I am six feet two inches tall and wore a permanent bruise for a while.

Around the yard, all the outbuildings were in much the same condition: basically sound in structure but neglected for so long that doors and windows were decaying, with electrical circuits and plumbing no longer working or in safe condition. Don't think that we were complaining; the lack of any modernisation was exactly what had attracted us in the first place, the whole unspoilt range of buildings possessing a great deal of charm and character.

It was the same story on the land itself. Two roadside gates were just about standing, but between the several small fields, not only the gates but even the posts had long since disappeared. The hedges had gaps and were largely untended. All of the land was permanent pasture: some low-lying along our six hundred yards of river frontage, with marshy areas full of rushes; the remainder rising fairly steeply from the valley floor, better drained and looking in good heart. For many years the grazing had been summer let for cattle only, with a little artificial fertilizer spread each spring and the rushes topped every autumn. No other chemicals had been used, nor any field ploughed, save a small part sown to oats during the second world war.

Close to the house lay a well-cultivated vegetable garden, with a few soft fruit bushes along one side and an ancient pear tree wrapping its branches around two walls of the stable. In the rick yard stood four cooking apple trees of great size and age.

We had already told the farmer who'd rented the grazing in the past that he could graze his cattle again during the coming summer season. This would give us time to sort ourselves out, take stock of our new situation and make a start on all the work that needed to be done. But we had scarcely unpacked when we were approached by a local man seeking some short-term grass keep for his

sheep until the end of January (this was in early December), when he would remove them for lambing. Taken by surprise, I said I would think about it and noted his telephone number. Discreet enquiries revealed that he had recently retired from farming to a bungalow in the nearby village. Having two daughters but no son to carry on the farm, he had sold everything except the small flock. We were keen to learn about sheep and here was a man with lifelong experience of them; it seemed ideal so I rang him and agreed terms.

Bill, our new tenant, looked over the land before bringing his animals and suggested fencing the road boundary, as the hedge was inadequate to prevent sheep from straying onto the road. I agreed, bought the materials and we did the work together. I had never done any fencing before and found it heavy work carrying the fifty metre rolls of galvanised mesh, making holes with a steel bar and - hardest of all - knocking the posts home with the sledge hammer. I had thought I was reasonably fit, but found myself struggling to keep pace with Bill's steady, unflinching work rate.

A few days later his flock of twenty-eight Suffolk type ewes arrived and set about our grass with gusto. With lambing approaching, Bill was soon trough feeding the sheep morning and evening; they quickly learned to follow the food bucket and if one went lame, it wasn't difficult to lead the flock into a building to deal with it.

All the time we watched and asked questions which Bill patiently answered. He soon realised the depth of our interest and, to cut a long story short, his flock never did leave to lamb elsewhere; they lambed in our outbuildings and we had first-hand practical experience from start to finish, gaining knowledge and confidence all the time. It was a very rewarding period for the whole family.

By the time the last ewe had lambed, we had dealt with a prolapsed cervix, ring womb, several cases of malpresentation, and lost just one lamb which was born completely encased in membranes, to suffocate during the few minutes when no-one was present. Bill's sheep had never had such close attention lavished upon them, nor, he admitted, had he ever achieved such a high success rate before.

In the thick of lambing, a set of triplets had arrived, all males and all healthy but one lamb showed little interest in suckling his mother and seemed to prefer nibbling at wellingtons. Soon Bill had marched into the kitchen and presented this one to Rosie for bottle rearing. He was installed in a tea chest in the scullery with the entire household revolving about his needs. Within two days, a repeat performance resulted in a second tea chest with bawling occupant appearing alongside.

As they grew stronger we moved them to a small strawed pen in an outhouse, and on nice days they were allowed out to follow us around the garden and yard. Our children adored them and played with them for hours on end. No doubt the novelty wears thin in time, but I have to admit that first experience of hand rearing was magical. The lucky pair, named Timmy and Chris, grew up almost as part of the family. Now they are almost useless wethers that I am strictly forbidden to consign to the freezer - I say almost because we do at least have their fleece each year. Of course we should have bottle reared ewe lambs, but both sets of triplets were all rams.

The one sour note in all this was when a protective ewe knocked down our son Martin, aged five, as he walked innocently between her and her lambs. He picked himself up and she flattened him again before Rosie could intervene. Not surprisingly this destroyed his confidence and for a long time afterwards he was wary of the sheep.

Throughout this same winter I attended an evening class at the local college. The tutor was an experienced small farmer and we studied tractor maintenance, chainsaw use, lambing and cattle rearing - all useful stuff which would come in handy in due course.

As for Bill, I think he was enjoying himself as much as we were. He had learned his farming in the horse-drawn era, and despite the great changes he had seen in agriculture during his lifetime, he retained a genuine affection for the old ways and took great pleasure in doing a task the traditional way rather than by modern machine. With no son to pass on his acquired wisdom to, perhaps I was the next best thing. I learned from him constantly and looked forward to our future in smallholding with increasing confidence.

Footnote: We just didn't think to ensure that Bill's sheep had been wormed before moving onto our pasture. Mistake! The land had been sheep-free for many years and was therefore clear of sheep parasites. Dosing any new introductions of sheep the night before turn-out would have maintained this happy state of affairs for as long as possible. But we were naïve and it was a unique opportunity missed.

Chapter 3
Blooming ragwort

Before we came to our smallholding, the grazing had been let for many years to a dairy farmer who had run young stock on the pasture during the summer months only. We were starting from scratch with no animals of our own and no plans to rush into buying too many, too soon, so it made sense to us to offer the arrangement for at least one more year to the same man, and this he readily accepted.

Then Bill arrived on the scene with his small flock of breeding ewes as already described, originally for winter grazing up to lambing time; but this developed into friendship, a sharing of his lifelong knowledge, and a desire to see the sheep year right through with his flock before we acquired many ewes of our own. This naturally would mean less grass available to the dairy farmer, but I discussed this with him and there was no problem; he would still run some of his cattle as usual on the eight acres most suited to his animals, while the sheep would graze the other eight acres of steeper land more suited to them. Terms and dates were agreed, and in due course a lorry arrived to unload eight in-calf heifers.

The days passed and the beasts grazed contentedly. The owner didn't call in to check them, which surprised us as he was well aware that we knew next to nothing about cattle, and were largely limited to counting each day to make sure they were still there. After nearly six weeks had passed, he called in for the first time and declared himself very pleased with their progress. At six weeks exactly, a lorry suddenly arrived to take them away unexpectedly, with a promise of replacement animals later on.

More weeks passed in a whirl of jobs and a procession of visitors from our former life. The grass in the vacant eight acres grew longer, rushes flourished in the damper areas, and a tall plant burst into brilliant yellow bloom in profusion. This was ragwort, and inexperienced though we were, even we knew that ragwort was poisonous.

Several weeks had gone by and still there was no sign of any more cattle arriving. Gradually the realisation dawned that we had a problem. We read up on it to discover that ragwort is at its most deadly when cut and dried, as in hay. We had a BIG problem, eight acres of unusable hay which we would have to cut, dry and burn, there was no other choice. But how?

We already had the use of a tractor, Bill's old around-the-yard Massey Ferguson that he hadn't sold on his retirement from full-time farming. Scouring the farm sales for an unwanted old finger beam mower to go with it, I was unexpectedly "given" one on permanent loan from another relative of the previous owner. It transpired that this mower had once belonged to the last miller to grind corn here, and had cut these acres many years before, passing on through two generations to finally return in my hour of need. It was a generous gesture so typical of the Devon folk who helped us in every way they could. Bill and I set to work mowing.

This was a thoroughly satisfying occupation, a few hours steady work transforming a field of waist high herbage into neatly laid rows on the ground - but that was the easy bit. Turning it by hand with pitchforks was slow, hard graft. In the nick of time, the search for implements at farm sales began to bear fruit, in the form of a hay turner and a low trailer with lades. Both were ancient, rusting and in need of some attention (and therefore cheap!) but nevertheless worked after a fashion. Soon I was whizzing over our acres flinging the "hay" to dry, and then "rowing up" ready for baling. Herein lay the next problem: we had no baler.

We made a start by hand, forking the stuff onto the trailer and carting to a central fire site. This was fine to start with, great fun for friends and visitors to help with (everyone loves a bonfire), but as the novelty waned and the sheer hard work began to tire us, we realised that we were hardly making any impression. September loomed with the prospect of cooler, wetter weather.

Just as our spirits were flagging, yet another farm sale yielded a baler. This was in much the same condition as the other machinery except that it didn't quite work. The vendor knew Bill and had assured us that it was working apart from a problem with the knotting mechanism, which had presumably driven him to exasperation and hence to a new baler.

We hitched it up and found that this information was correct; it picked up and thrust the material into the baling chamber all right, and even tied the knot around the completed bale. But then it failed to cut the cord so that as more material forced into the chamber, the cord tensioned until it broke at the weakest point - the knot holding the first bale together. Investigation revealed a small knife blade rusted away to a blunt edge. This was sharpened by hand, refitted and hey presto: we had bales with cord round, instead of without. With that one adjustment, the baler went on to pickup the remaining acres in no time at all. It was such a relief, like the cavalry arriving in an old Western. Even Bill was impressed as it happily gobbled up mountains of rushes, ragwort and long grass over rough ground. The resulting bales were carted to the fire site, stacked, cut open and burned.

Wet weather closed in with one hundred bales remaining and these we reluctantly left in a low stack to dispose of in some other way. Unable to gain access to them over wet ground until the following summer, we found to our

surprise that they rotted down to very little where they stood. Livestock then trod the pile flat, leaving us to simply pick out the baler cord.

So ended a nightmare period, with a lesson hard learned - we vowed never to allow such a situation to develop again. It was annoying to be let down by the dairy farmer, who had failed to honour his grazing agreement with us. Equally I blamed myself for not acting sooner to rectify this by offering the grazing elsewhere. The ragwort was nobody's fault, just a symptom of the neglect of our pasture for years past, but we noticed that smaller amounts of the stuff grew on neighbouring farms where the cattle grazed around it, leaving the plants themselves standing in isolation for easy cutting once animals were moved on.

In fact, the ragwort problem was quite easily solved, and although this is jumping ahead with our story, it is worth including here for anyone out there who is struggling with the stuff. Simply cutting it before the seeds have dispersed is a big help; marsh ragwort is biennial so it takes two years cutting to be effective. The full answer came from John Seymour's book *The Lore of the Land*, in which he has this to say of ragwort:

"Sheep love it when it is young and by grazing sheep on it in the early summer you will completely eliminate it, probably in one season, certainly in two. I have never known this fail."

This has certainly worked for us. We stocked heavily with sheep in the late spring/early summer, grazed it hard, the animals flourished and the ragwort disappeared that year. And good riddance!

Chapter 4
Hens, ducks and veg

We had kept a few laying hens in our previous back garden and were keen to run a small free-range flock now that we had the space. Our reading told us that modern hybrid birds were the ones to choose for maximum egg production, and Bill's experience confirmed this. He had kept layers all his life and tried most of the common breeds in his time, but his present half-a-dozen hybrids were outlaying anything he'd kept before. These were in their first year and produced six eggs most days, with an occasional five thrown in. He ordered a dozen point-of-lay pullets for us from the same local supplier. Our intention was to have enough eggs for household use with sufficient surplus for sale to cover feeding costs.

I converted an old pig sty into luxurious quarters for them, with generous straw over the concrete floor, free-standing perches on legs (rather like a table with no top to it), four nest boxes salvaged from another barn, and the old feeding door by the trough removed and replaced by a metal grille for ventilation. In

theory this was large enough to keep the hens shut in on wet winter days, otherwise the door opened onto the fields beyond the yard.

The birds were duly collected and installed. They laid three eggs in the back of the car, more in the nest boxes and were soon churning out eleven or twelve every day. One interesting thing we noticed was the change in quality of these eggs from day one onwards. The pullets had been reared on deep litter in a large barn with no access to the outside world, and fed on commercial rations. We free-ranged them on grass and fed layers pellets in the mornings, mixed corn and scraps in the evenings, but deliberately less than their full daily requirement to encourage them to find the balance for themselves. And they seemed to do just that, busy scratching and searching for much of the day in between sunbathing and dust baths.

The first eggs were like so many shop-bought ones - a watery white, pale yellow yolk, with little flavour and just a hint of fishiness (perhaps from previous fish meal rations). Over the next few days we saw them change to a thicker consistency, with deepening yellow yolks and a transformation in taste. There is no doubt about it as far as we are concerned: free-range eggs win hands down.

The ducks arrived next. A new acquaintance told us of a brood of ducklings looking for a good home, and did we want any? Well, we had planned to have some ducks at some time in the future, so affirmative noises were made and in no time at all there were seven fluffy yellow Aylesbury ducklings tucked up safe and warm under a heat lamp. They'd been hatched by a broody hen and varied in size, but all seemed strong and healthy. I put them in the second pig sty next door to the hens, within a small rat-proof run of metal grille sides and top, and deep straw on the cold concrete floor. We read with surprise that ducklings reared apart from their mothers must not immerse themselves in water for the first several weeks of life, so the drinking water was supplied in a small dish, frequently topped up.

Starting on chick crumbs and later building up to scraps and grower rations, they ate an incredible amount of food for their size but grew correspondingly fast. They graduated to a daytime run outside on grass, and once old enough to take to water moved on again to the millpond across the yard from their pig sty, free-ranging from there onto the fields beyond. Of course we shut them in every night away from foxes.

At this stage they looked identical, resplendent in snow-white plumage but with no clues as to which were ducks and which were drakes. This was a slight problem as we thought we might keep the ducks for egg laying, with one drake perhaps, and eat any surplus drakes. We were assured that all would be revealed in time, as indeed it was; there were two ducks and five drakes, and once they had realised their differences the ducks began to have a bit of a rough time from the queue of admirers. Soon we were enjoying our very first home-produced

roast duck (or rather drake) and delicious it was too, though it must be said that the carcass provided far less meat than a table chicken of similar weight. The bones made lovely soup and the down and smaller feathers improved our duvet, so not much was wasted.

By this time the vegetable garden was well "on stream", supplying a succession of produce for the kitchen. We had inherited a long-established patch of about twenty yards square containing a few very old soft fruit bushes and bounded by a four foot high earth bank. Our soil type is fairly heavy clay over rock, so drainage is generally poor, but this garden had been cultivated over the years to a decent soil structure. There was evidence of sand worked in, not only to lighten the soil but to counter the acidity, for the beach at Bude not many miles distant has sand made up of crushed shell fragments rather than rock alone, and was used locally in centuries past to sweeten the land, until displaced by lime.

My predecessor here was now in his eighties and enjoyed something of a reputation locally as a gardener. He told me that it was not an early location, being in the frost pocket of the river valley floor, nor could he grow carrots, being beaten by the dreaded fly despite all the traditional and chemical remedies he had tried. He'd used a little artificial fertiliser and practised no crop rotation.

I foresaw problems of soil compaction on this fairly heavy ground and decided to use the bed system to overcome them. Beds of four feet in width were marked out aligned north to south, with paths between alternately eighteen inches and two feet wide. The wider paths would give wheelbarrow access to each bed on one side, the narrower ones provided foot access and were sufficient to work from comfortably. Then came the problem of hand weeding the harvest from years of rotovator use. It was a long job but by doing a bit most days we got there in the end. I had no muck available yet to feed the soil, but did have some compost brought from the last place and supplemented this with fish, blood and bone meal. In the early spring I began to plant.

Many of the locals here run a garden but, to a man, use the rotovator and row system, so there were many puzzled stares over the garden bank, which

happens to border the road into the village. Bill was intrigued by my beds and kept a close eye on my progress. When the broad beans showed their first leaves above the soil, he commented that here was a different variety to any he'd seen before. They were ordinary enough longpods so I looked too; the leaf edges were scalloped so evenly that it looked natural!

The culprit responsible for this damage was the pea or bean weevil, a mud-brown pest that I had not encountered before. They live in the soil at the base of the plants during the day, emerging at night to feed on the leaves. Of course, their preference is for the young, tender parts of the growing tips and I soon found that the plants could not outgrow the damage; they were simply standing still. Unwilling to use chemicals, I spent hours on hands and knees collecting and killing the things from the soil and leaves, but I made little impression. A nicotine solution was the organic answer, but we don't smoke and local enquiries failed to produce the necessary quantity of cigarette ends. A mild pesticide had no effect. I gave in and drenched the soil over a very small area around each plant with a synthetic garden insecticide. It worked and we had our bean crop in the end. There must have been a plague in my vegetable patch that year, for although damage from this weevil is quite commonly seen locally, it has not been such a problem for me since, nor have "last resort" chemicals been used again.

Despite the advice about frost pockets, early potatoes were set to show the first week in May. The initial vigour of growth fizzled out too soon as the foliage yellowed and failed on many plants. Digging revealed low yields of smallish tubers carrying lots of tiny white cysts; I hadn't seen this before either but my books identified eelworm, a build-up of which is attributable to lack of crop rotation. I'd have to experiment another year to see if there were any clean parts within the garden where potatoes had not been grown in recent years.

And despite the advice about carrot fly, I sowed a succession of roots and surrounded each sowing with a vertical barrier several inches high, made up of small glass panes that I happened to have handy at the time - an organic tip I had read about that denies access to the low-flying pest. The resulting crop was heavy, delicious and almost undamaged. I hadn't the heart to tell the old boy.

Footnote: Our subsequent experience with highly developed laying hybrid hens was that they seemed to burn themselves out after one laying season, with some failing to survive beyond their first moult or if they did, laying noticeably fewer eggs. Of course, these birds were specifically bred for maximum first year egg production in caged systems. Nowadays there are alternative hybrids developed for free-range conditions, with a heavier bodyweight, closer feathering and still-impressive egg laying abilities.

Chapter 5
The flood

One of the many things that first attracted us to our Devon smallholding was the six hundred yards of river frontage that forms one boundary to the land. The Tamar is an important river in its lower reaches with an historic port at its junction with the sea, and good runs of salmon and sea trout; but here in the upper reaches it is little more than a stream meandering carelessly through the valley.

It chatters sparkling over gravel shallows, glides smoothly through the shadows of overhanging bushes, and drops into deep, mysterious pools. Small brown trout dimple the surface taking flies, brilliantly coloured dragonflies flash above the water, grey heron and kingfisher hunt for their living. It is never still, never silent, always alive with wildlife and colour at every season of the year. We derive great pleasure from walking its banks in the course of our daily lives, and yet there is a drawback - the flooding it sometimes brings to the valley and to some of our land.

Our first winter here was unusually mild and wet. At times the rain was heavy and prolonged, with the result that the river flooded over its banks and covered the low-lying land with water. We noticed that there was something like twenty four hours between the onset of heavy rain and the river leaving its banks; it seemed to take that long for all the myriad ditches and feeder streams to fill up and in their turn to fill the main channel to capacity. Even ferocious weather that winter seemed unable to cause flooding any quicker than this.

Some flood prevention work was carried out some seven or eight years ago to relieve cottages in the village centre from a regular soaking. A small island just below the bridge was removed completely to assist the flow through the arch, and a high bank was thrown up on the village side of the river so that floodwater would spill over first to the opposite side, into farmland. The locals assured us that things had not been so bad since, and only once during the wet winter did the floodwater lap over the road crossing the bridge to a depth of a few inches; no houses were affected. Even at this reduced level, the flooding would cover about four acres of land on our two riverside meadows (called 'hams' locally). It is not a matter of merely inches of water, for with some variation in the field surface it lies to a depth of three or four feet in places, and all moving powerfully downstream. Obviously livestock must be moved from these fields when flooding threatens, but this was something we had to expect and learn to live with.

The summer of 1988 passed, and when we left the village pub late one evening in October, the steady rain that met our faces caused no real concern. There were sheep in the Bridge Ham, seventeen young ewes and well-grown lambs. The ground was already wet from rain a few days earlier, but the river was running low down within its banks at normal summer level. Even if it rained all night, there would be time enough to move the sheep during the morning before the flood could follow by the evening. I fell asleep without a second thought on the matter....

Dull torchlight lit the room as Rosie shook me back to wakefulness. In that strange state between deep sleep and full consciousness, I struggled to make sense of what she was saying. The urgency in her voice suddenly got through to me and I began to take it in: the river already over its banks... tried to bring out the sheep on her own but couldn't... water deep and rising fast...

"Come on, Alan, we've got to save the sheep!"

Almost awake now, I began to pull on some clothes and glanced at the clock - it was five am. This was impossible, it only began to rain seven hours ago. Then I became aware of the noise outside, the wind battering torrential rain against the window. I looked at Rosie, the soaked hair plastered to her face, the desperate expression in her eyes, and I knew it was true. My mind was starting to function - don't panic, pull on the waterproof gear, find the big torches, work out a plan of action. One step out of the front door and I was finally wide awake as the wind and rain tore at my face and hands; it was wild and no mistake. Through the yard and across the small paddock, our torch-beams picked out streams of water overflowing from the ditch at the top of the field and flowing down to the gateway of the bridge ham. We sloshed through with the water just under the tops of our wellingtons, and then paused while I took in the incredible scene.

There was water everywhere, spilling from side ditches, pouring through gateways, blanketing the grass before me. I knew the field well enough by day but now, in pitch darkness, our torch beams reflecting from a continuous sheet of water, it took on a strange and very different appearance. Where the river channel should have been was a raging torrent of swirling foam and flood-borne debris, snaking through a shining mirror of calmer water.

We set off down the ham towards the bridge some two hundred yards distant, keeping to the higher ground and sloshing ankle deep through sodden grass with the leaves just breaking the surface. At one point the land narrows to a neck only a few yards wide between the hedge on one side and the river, bending sharply, on the other. The passage of animals over many years had worn away the topsoil to form a bowl dipping below the rest of the field, laced with the exposed roots of trees. Now it posed a trap for the unwary. We edged around it by the hedge, while the swollen river raged past close by, angry and menacing.

Beyond this fearful place we found the flock, their eyes glowing in our torch-beams, standing frightened and confused in shallow water. My mind was racing to find a way out of this nightmare situation. How were we to move them safely up the field to the only exit (the gate we had entered by) without them panicking into the unseen river channel and certain death? As we hesitated, talking quietly to them for the re-assurance of familiar voices, the very thing happened that I was trying to avoid - they raced off as one into the darkness.

Stumbling, splashing, half-running after them, we shone our torch beams on the main channel in the hope that they would see the danger. We need not have worried - being creatures of great habit, they followed the route they knew up the ham, half-swimming through the deep pool at the neck, on through the lake that was now their field until they stopped just short of the gateway and safety, crowding instead on to a small island of grass as yet uncovered by the water.

Struggling up behind them, gasping for breath, we could not understand why they had baulked at this last hurdle until, standing alongside, we realised how much the flood had risen in the short space of time since we had first passed through the gateway. Now it was too deep for them to wade; like the narrow neck of the field, it was worn down by constant passage and low-lying. They would have to swim across, but try as we did, we could not move them another inch.

In desperation I grabbed the nearest ewe and dragged her into the water. She was rigid with fear and fought against me with all her strength. Water flooded into my boots as we wrestled slowly through the gateway until, with a last effort, we foundered through shallows on the other side and on to dry land, and safety. She stood like a statue where I released her while I waded back to fetch another. Then she bleated, again and again, the first sound that any of them had made, and a most astonishing thing happened: the rest of the flock, which had been rooted to the spot, dived as one into the flood and swam through the gateway to join her. We followed too, relieved and thankful that the nightmare was over.

We put the flock into the stable on straw bedding to dry off, then dried ourselves and returned to bed, tired and for my part, feeling very foolish that I had allowed the situation to develop in the first place.

By daybreak the water lay waist deep over the ham. By mid-morning the flood was over the road on both sides of the bridge, impassable except by tractor. There was something approaching a carnival atmosphere in the village as everyone came down to see the flooding, the worst since the flood prevention work had been carried out several years before. It was the speed of it that staggered

me - ten hours from low trickle to flooded valley! Wading through to stand on the bridge, we gazed in awe at the scene of our rescue operation just a few hours earlier. It had been so close to disaster.

After this experience, we made it an unbreakable rule to withdraw grazing animals from the two riverside fields before dark onto higher ground, returning them the next morning if conditions allow. It's one more job to do each day, but at least we can sleep soundly in our beds.

Chapter 6
New skills on the land

The largest piece of ground I had looked after in the past was no more than a good-sized garden. Now the prospect of caring for sixteen and a half acres was somewhat daunting.

Fencing was an early priority. The hedge adjoining the public road was inadequate to contain sheep, so under the guidance of Bill (whose sheep they were) we erected a woven wire mesh fence inside the offending hedge. His method was first to set out the intermediate posts, with one every four paces. A hole was made with a heavy iron bar worked vigorously from side to side to enlarge the hole and firm the sides once each downward thrust had been made. When the hole was deep enough, around eighteen inches, the four foot six inch long sawn and tanalised post was dropped in (pointed end first!) and driven home with the sledge hammer until firm.

Next, one end of the roll of wire mesh was stapled firmly to the gatepost at the starting point, and the roll was unwound to the first few posts. With one man pulling his weight to tighten the wire at the first post, the other man drove home staples to fix firmly to that post. We then moved on to each post in turn repeating this procedure at each one. Finally the far end of the mesh was stapled to another gatepost. This first run of fence was pretty straight, but beyond the land rose in uneven contours while the hedge curved through more than a right angle. There were no more handy gateposts either. Bill drove a larger five foot six inch post at the two end points but otherwise proceeded as before. It was more difficult to pull the wire mesh taut as the fence rose and turned, and in places we had to settle for the best we could manage.

It looked a reasonable job when finished, but in time some drawbacks became evident. Sheep pushed their heads through the mesh to nibble the greenery beyond, and put their weight against it, stretching and slackening the wire and loosening some of the intermediate posts. With the staples driven home at every post, it was a difficult job to re-tension the fence and the wire's galvanised coating was damaged in removing staples, so hastening rust. The five foot six inch end posts proved inadequate to hold firm against tension and gradually pulled over a little, slackening the fence again. But to be fair, it did keep the sheep in.

Before putting up any fencing on my own, I read up on the subject and looked at the work of professional contractors locally. The general consensus of opinion seemed to favour a substantial straining post at each end and at each change of direction, braced for rigidity against adjacent intermediate posts. The wire was fixed firmly only at these posts and strained taut; then at all intermediate posts, staples were driven only halfway in to facilitate easier removal or re-tensioning in the future. As we built up our own sheep flock, which could push through the gappy hedges with relative ease, I began to erect some internal fencing incorporating these features.

We had joined a smallholders group and began to benefit from meeting with more experienced members. The group owned a wire strainer that I borrowed, and the group organisers kindly lent me their own large rubber maul or mallet. Suitably equipped, I put up a hundred yard run of fence along the edge of a gently curving watercourse. The rubber maul seemed extremely unwieldy at first after the sledgehammer, but I quickly found that it was just as effective at driving the posts home without the sledgehammer's drawback of splitting the post tops. I was so impressed that I bought my own. The wire strainer proved fiddly to set up and use; tensioning one horizontal wire at a time, I found it difficult to obtain an even strain over the full height of the mesh.

With perseverance this was overcome and the resulting fence looked fine. Time showed up the shortcomings again. The problem lay in the curve of the fence - in soft ground the intermediate posts tended to give under the tension until it was removed. Slack wire again, but it still kept the sheep in.

Re-tensioning was still fiddly with all the staples to remove at one end, so I devised a simpler method of straining the wire for my next fence. The end posts were substantial and strutted as before, all intermediate posts were driven into position except one at a curve in the fence about midway along its length. The wire was stapled firmly to one end post, run all the way to the far end loosely stapled to each intermediate, then fixed firmly to that end post. Now the final intermediate post was positioned so as to draw the whole run of wire tight, a long iron bar being used to lever the mesh into position for stapling. This critical post was strengthened by tying or strutting to a firm support back in the hedge.

Of course this fence suffered the same weakness of some intermediate posts yielding slightly under the tension on the curves, but it was more easily retightened by moving the critical post with its partly driven staples. So far, on our uneven land with curving fence lines, this is looking the most promising method, but I am still learning.

Gates were a rarity on our holding. The essential "boundary" gates fronting the yard and the road were still standing, just, but elsewhere several other gateways between fields were mostly devoid even of posts, the adjacent banks and hedges worn back by the passage of animals, the gateways themselves hollowed in the centre and culverts beneath blocked or collapsed. In winter these became permanent muddy morasses. Something had to be done if we were to contain our stock and rotate the grazing.

I found one gate lying in the hedge, propped there and forgotten long ago. It was rotted or broken in a few places, but a couple of hours work patching and strengthening produced a serviceable gate. Its hinges fitted the crooks of an ancient, hollowing post in the nearest gateway to its resting place in the hedge, so there it was re-hung. There was no latching post, however, so Bill showed me his way of setting one in place. The required position was marked by offering up the gate, and we then began to dig, first with shovels, then breaking up the harder subsoil and rock with an iron bar. The loose spoil was shovelled out and the iron bar brought into play alternately as the hole deepened. It was slow, hard work.

Eventually our efforts had produced a hole three feet deep and fifteen inches square - and I had learned the value of a traditional Devon shovel. Bill's well-worn example had a long straight shaft set at an angle to the blade, which tapered to a point. Once the hole had gone below a certain depth, my builders shovel and garden spade were confined too near the vertical to scoop out spoil, while the Devon shovel with its cranked blade just kept on going. The pointed shape was ideal for working into the corners or under stones. It was the right tool for the job, and I soon bought one of my own.

The post was an old but sound railway sleeper, bought cheaply at a farm sale. I cut a point on the top end to shed rainwater, then lowered the other end into the hole. We checked for position against the gate, then shovelled a little earth back into the hole and tamped it down hard with the iron bar. A few more inches of earth, more tamping and so on up to ground level, checking periodically that the post remained vertical. Bill said that if the tamping was done thoroughly enough, all the soil removed in digging the hole should go back in around the post. It did, and the post was firm. A staple was driven in to accept the latch of the gate to complete the job.

Next I turned my attention to the gateway itself. An old culvert carrying rainwater drainage beneath it was blocked, so that water poured over the gateway instead. I got down into the ditch on either side, dug down through the silt and debris until I found the mouth of the pipe, then rodded through until the blockage of twigs and leaves gave way. Using Bill's tractor and transport box, we transported several loads of rubble across from the yard and spread it carefully in the hollow through the gateway and into the field on either side, taking care to slope the surface for rainwater run-off and filling in with fine debris and earth to bind the rubble into a firm surface. This quickly grassed over and "disappeared", banishing the muddy morass problem. Finally, I blocked the small gap between the new latching post and the existing hedge with a few strands of barbed wire, as a temporary measure (yes, they are still there two years later!)

There were no more gates to be found in the hedges, and none worth having at farm sales, so it looked as though I would need to buy or make the rest. Shopping around for the best value in wooden gates I discovered gate kits. These comprise all the timber you need plus the nuts and bolts to assemble the gate. At half the cost of a ready-made gate this had to be worth a try, so I bought a ten-foot version in the Devon style, traditional to this area.

The stiles were already mortised to accept the pales, so there was little carpentry involved; it was a fairly straightforward matter of laying out all the parts and assembling on the ground, drilling holes through each mortise joint and bolting up. I did go to the luxury of forming a dovetail joint where the diagonal brace met the hanging stile, a strengthening feature observed on old gates locally which seemed to have stood the test of time. I bought a new strap hinge for the top hanging position, but made do with a rusty sale bargain for the lower hinge which is less critical.

When I came to hang the gate, the top crook was a new threaded type driven right through the post and locked by a nut and washer on the far side, giving strength and fine adjustment, while the lower crook was an old salvaged one with a spike just driven into position. Hanging and latching posts came from farm sales, at a fraction of the new cost - railway sleepers in good condition, and sections of oak tree trunk roughly squared. I was pleased with the first effort and went on to do several more in due course along the same lines, at an overall cost of £35 to £40 per gateway, as opposed to at least £80 "off the shelf". Surely one of the many skills in smallholding is to do for one pound what any fool can do for two?

Chapter 7
Banks, hedges and trees

The making and hanging of gates was only half the story on our smallholding. Some of the gateways themselves had lacked gates or even posts for so long that the passage of animals had worn away the traditional Devon earth banks on either side to leave a gap of up to twenty feet wide. With a ten-foot gate now freshly hung between its posts, the task remained to make good the banks in stock proof fashion.

A few small gaps were blocked with wire or rail fencing between the new post and eroded bank, but this looks the temporary measure that it is. For a "main thoroughfare" gateway seen and used daily, I decided to tackle the job of restoring the earth banks and facing with dry stone walling, or stone hedging as it is known in these parts. I had a quantity of stone salvaged from a collapsed wall, so the raw materials were free, as was the advice from my new friend Alf. It was commonsense really - dig out a footing trench down to firm subsoil and set out a foundation course of the largest stones within it, building up from this with staggered joints between courses (as in brickwork).

I set to work in this fashion, using dry earth in place of mortar to bed down

each stone and filling in the bank behind as the wall rose. It was a long job, made longer by two factors. One was the irregular shaped stone, which gave rise to much offering up and trial and error before each would fit snugly on top of the previous course. By comparison, the small amount of square-faced stone that I had available was easier and quicker to place. The other factor was having to dig and wheelbarrow the earth infill from some distance away, whereas a handy pile tipped on site would have saved hours of marching backwards and forwards.

It turned out that after rebuilding a semicircular end up to the gatepost on each side in stonework, there was no stone left to face the remaining repair work, but this coincided with a request from Rosie to strip some turf from an area of rough grass in the garden to create a new bed for her plants. Cutting the turfs carefully in neat rectangles with plenty of soil attached gave me the ideal material for turf facing the repaired bank. The same procedure was used as for stonework, setting a foundation course below existing ground level then building upwards in level courses with staggered joints, ramming earth infill behind as work progressed.

There are two schools of opinion on the orientation of these turfs; some lay them grass upwards, as dug, thus presenting an earth face to the bank which will quickly sprout grass cover from all the roots it contains, others lay them

grass looking outwards so that the face is instantly green. I tried both, and time has shown the grass-outward method to be better, not only in appearance but also in withstanding wear and tear from the sheep. Either way, turfs are easier and much quicker to build with than stone, although I have no doubt which material will stand the longest.

When at last the work was finished, I removed the temporary fence wire that kept the sheep away from the site area. The flock came over to investigate and one of our Shetland ewes jumped effortlessly to the top of the new bank to admire the view! So I have to suffer the indignity of barbed wire along the top until a sufficient hedge has grown to render the bank finally stock proof.

This brings us on to hedges and hedge laying, another new skill with which I quickly had to grapple on account of the neglected and gappy hedgerows which both surrounded and criss-crossed our holding. My initial efforts were directed at blocking the gaps through which the sheep had forced, and consisted of laying a nearby thorn bush across the hole before tying firmly in position with baler twine. Of course, there wasn't always a convenient nearby thorn, and I soon learned that if the gap was not blocked thoroughly, the sheep would test the repair until it gave way. Conversely if it held, determined animals would then find the next weak point alongside before making a new gap! Patching a strong hedge was worthwhile - patching a weak one definitely wasn't, it was back to fencing to contain the stock until the hedge could grow up sufficiently to be re-laid effectively.

The Devon method of hedge laying is straightforward enough. Unwanted growth is removed from both faces of the earth bank, surplus growth not required for laying is cut out from the growth along the top, then the remainder is laid by cutting the stems most, but not all, of the way through before lowering almost horizontally to the bank top. Tying with baler twine at intervals gives a firm finish to the job; or stakes are cut from the surplus growth and driven in to hold the laid stems in place. The result is not the artistic woven pattern of some other counties, but in combination with the high bank, it is stock proof and forms a thick hedge of natural appearance again within a few seasons if not trimmed.

One thing our smallholding lacked, to our eyes anyway, was woodland. There were some lovely individual trees, mainly oak and ash with some beech, in hedgerows or along the river's edge, but no copses. So we decided to plant a few field corners and grow our own, motivated by a whole host of reasons: landscape value, woodland plants and wildlife, coppice for hurdles and firewood, timber for posts and gates. Yes, it's a long-term view, but we aim to be here for a long time! And if we don't enjoy all the benefits, our children will.

I fenced off the chosen areas against stock and bought our first trees, ash and southern beech (*Nothofagus procera*, a South American relative of our own beech but much faster growing). These were bare-rooted "whips" of two to three feet in height; small enough to be cheap, to require no staking and, so the theory goes, to establish and grow quickly, thereby soon outpacing larger, more expensive trees which are set back by the shock of moving. I followed the advice of books by stripping an area of turf (around one square yard), digging a pit about fifteen inches square to accept the roots, breaking up the subsoil with a fork before setting the tree vertically in position and filling around the roots with soil, heeling in firmly. After watering, a sheet of black plastic was set in place over the grass-free square yard around the tree to suppress weeds.

Some new friends were clearing a former quarry, now invaded by silver birch and hazel scrub, and at their invitation I also dug up a number of small young trees of these two species from the woodland edge. I was immediately struck by the contrast between the vigorous, spreading root systems of these trees and the spindly, almost rootless things I had just spent hard-earned money on. I had been assured that the restricted roots on these commercial whips were deliberate policy for better transplanting - but one year later, most of the beech had died while the ash remained exactly the same size, surviving but without making new growth. The birch and hazel dug up with complete root systems had flourished and made obvious progress. I made sure that any trees purchased from then on had a conventional healthy root system to see them off to a good start.

Chapter 8
Machinery

We came to our smallholding armed only with hand tools from our previous gardening, but soon found that it was not physically possible to manage the land as we wanted by our muscle power alone. Initially we let the grazing and Bill, our tenant, brought along his old tractor plus transport box, giving us the use of these in unspoken part payment for our grass. We began to look for suitable implements at farm sales and through local enquiry.

First to turn up was the finger-beam mower, loaned to me as already mentioned. It had been well looked after during its long working life and required only routine oil and grease before starting to cut. Had we needed to buy one, similar "grass machines" in working order were fetching around £60.

An old and rusting hay turner cost £42 at a farm sale. There were two broken tines and a bent arm but otherwise it was sound; replacement parts were soon found to repair it to full working order again. A trailer bought at the same time cost £100 - and came in handy for transporting the hay turner back home! The trailer wasn't rusty, but a few of the wooden base boards were rotten. At twelve feet long by five feet wide, and low-slung at the axle height of its wheels, it came with lades front and back to make it ideal for carting bales. A few hours work soon patched up the faulty boarding.

An old and rusting baler cost £80 at another sale, and I have already described how a problem with the knotter mechanism was readily overcome to provide a working machine at a modest price. Chain harrows always seemed to fetch too much money at farm sales, but I found a set eventually for a reasonable £10 through the local smallholders group. The harrows were minus a few links and the spreader bars were bent a little, but they were adequate to do their job.

As our sheep flock grew in size and Bill's gradually declined through sale of the older ewes, he offered us the chance to purchase his tractor, a Massey Ferguson 65 that he had originally purchased new in 1964. It had its faults, but better the devil you know. . . . £300 eventually changed hands to complete our capital outlay for the time being. We had spent £532 in all, and were now equipped to tackle most of the jobs around the holding.

Our pasture management includes topping to remove flowering stalks and uneaten tussocks, weed cutting (especially thistles), and harrowing to spread dung and encourage fresh growth. Our harvest is hay: cut, turned, baled and carted to store for the winter. We do much the same with soft rush, *Juncus effusus*, which grows in abundance on the lower wet ground; cut in late summer, turned until golden brown, baled and carted to dry store, it serves admirably as winter bedding in place of straw.

On top of this are all the fetching and carrying tasks around the fields: gates and posts, stone and turf for walling, rubble for surfacing gateways, pipes for drains and culverts, fence wire and posts plus the tools to put them up, logs for the fire, a sick sheep in the furthest field, a fallen tree to pull from the river, and so on - all so much quicker and easier with the tractor and box or trailer, and some impossible without. There's diesel to buy, but agricultural grade is cheap and it goes a long way. There's some care and maintenance required, but because everything is ancient, this is usually straightforward, with simple, robust mechanics bolted, riveted or welded. There's little to go wrong and when it does, it's mostly commonsense to put it right again.

There are other ways of tackling the major tasks without buying your own equipment. Some smallholders manage with the help of a friendly neighbour, but clearly something has to be offered in return, perhaps by helping out at his peak workloads. Contractors will do it all, at a price and maybe not at the best time because with a small acreage you are bottom of the priority list.

Our own choice is to be independent as far as possible. It is a valuable asset to be able to do what you wish at your own pace and at a time that suits you. I admit to a practical background in mechanical engineering which obviously helps, but any reasonably practical person can handle the maintenance and simple breakdowns. I make no suggestion that the above prices are those you should be looking to pay for implements today; they are simply a statement of what we paid at the time. I am quite sure that it was money well spent - the harvest of hay and rushes alone have more than repaid the initial outlay; all the rest is a bonus.

Chapter 9
Building

The house and outbuildings on our smallholding were basically sound for the most part, just neglected for a long time and in need of maintenance. The exception to this was the stable, a two-storey traditional structure with stone walls, cobbled ground floor and slate roof. One gable end wall had largely collapsed into the field beyond, revealing a previous, inadequate, attempt at repair work. The unsupported roof timbers at this end were sagging, and the prevailing winds drove the Devon rain onto the wooden hayloft floor. This had to be dealt with before another winter passed. I had no experience at all of building skills and we were up to our ears trying to do everything else around the holding, so we called in the builders. Rosie had her eye on the hayloft as her craft workshop, while the ground floor would house sheep at lambing time, so the cost could be justified.

The builders knocked out the loose blocks and stone down to a firm foundation, then began to rebuild the wall in stone. I hadn't seen this done before and learned a great deal watching them. The older, more experienced craftsman laid the outer course while the younger man laid the inner; the gap between the outer and inner courses was filled with small stone and mortar as the work progressed upwards, binding the two foot thickness of wall solidly together. The roof timbers were jacked up to their original positions and their ends let into the new stone wall as it rose to meet them. Missing roof slates were replaced to complete the job. The rubble that remained I put to good use, filling in eroded gateways around the holding. The newness of the repairs has mellowed with time to give a very satisfactory result.

The farmhouse itself we lived in just as it was for twelve months before doing anything to it; we have found before that you need to do this to avoid making mistakes, as things that seem like a good idea at first sight gradually change complexion with time. During this first year we did some research into the building techniques and finishes required on an old house of mainly cob on a stone base. It had been modernised in the early 1930's according to the fashion of the time: thatched roof removed and replaced by asbestos slate, pebbledash finish to the walls, sash windows, small open fire with tiled surround covering (we hoped) an inglenook fireplace, and so on. Everything now needed attention except the roof, which remained remarkably good - a testimony to the skill of its creator who is still remembered with admiration locally.

A grant was available from the local council because we had no "proper" bathroom and what the estate agents euphemistically call "private drainage". The

bathroom was a small tin-roofed, single brick walled extension built on the back of the house, from which the bathwater emptied directly onto the ground outside; while the drain from the toilet led towards a mythical cesspit at some unknown location in the field - before turning sharply and emptying into the river! This we only discovered when the system first became blocked. I will spare you the details but at least this entitled us to the maximum grant.

There were strings attached to the grant that made us pause for thought. A man from the Planning Department surveyed the house to draw up a long list of improvements and works needed, all of which had to be tackled to qualify for the grant, yet some we would not choose to do if left to ourselves. Discussions led to a further site visit from the head man himself, and he proved very sympathetic to our arguments, eventually waiving those things like raising door and ceiling heights to modern standard or lifting slate flags, which would have destroyed much of the character. So plans were drawn up and a grant applied for.

We discovered, too late, that we had engaged the wrong architect for the job. Well qualified and professional, he had no real sympathy for old buildings and traditional methods. Suitably informed by *The House Restorer's Guide* (ISBN 0-7153-8386-8) by Hugh Lander - essential reading for anyone contemplating the restoration of an old building - I persuaded him to change a number of details in the specification that he drew up for us. We were determined to recapture as much as possible of the features and character of the house that now lay hidden under the 1930's facade.

A recommendation led me to a small local builder who seemed ideal for the job. He was quite happy for us to work alongside his own few men to keep our costs down as far as possible, and for me to supply second-hand materials where appropriate. As the work was mainly inside and he was relatively quiet for the winter months, we agreed to tackle the work in one big hit, moving out to leave an empty house for nine weeks from January to March. We all felt this was better than trying to live in while the work went on around us - that way it takes longer, costs more, and strains relationships.

I didn't wait until January to remove the fireplace. With winter approaching

we fancied a wood burning stove to make more efficient use of our fuel, so one day while Rosie was out I began to probe with a small crowbar - just to see how firmly it was attached! She returned to find the tiled surround lying in the yard outside, and the front room full of rubble, dust and soot. Many barrow loads were carted out before the full size of the original opening was revealed. There was slight disappointment in that the original beam had gone, to be replaced by a steel lintel with rough brickwork above. Not to worry, a false wooden beam slung below this looked fine and plaster would hide the rest. I fitted the woodburner and register plate to keep us snug until January.

At the appointed time we moved out to a self-catering holiday let establishment within sight of our place, just a couple of fields away. Normally closed for the winter, the owners very kindly accommodated us but required us to vacate in mid-March for their first bookings of the season. This gave us a deadline to work towards, which was no bad thing.

Every morning I would breakfast early and walk across the fields to check and feed the livestock before the building team arrived. The sheep soon learned this and they would call to me as soon as I appeared in view on the driveway of the holiday place, some two hundred yards distant. Later, we read in a farming publication how sheep have such poor eyesight that they cannot distinguish a familiar human from an unknown one at a few paces! Anyone who has kept tame sheep will know otherwise.

The house was soon stripped to a shell, with all plaster removed inside and out, ceilings down, floors up, partition walls out. Painted doors went away for stripping, windows came out, lean-to porches were pulled down. It was savage treatment, but we were relieved to find that the real fabric of the house, the walls and beams, were mainly sound. Weak areas were strengthened, cracks filled, and the work of restoring began.

Woodworm was banished with a "bat-friendly" chemical, rising damp blocked with silicone injection, wet concrete floors dug out and replaced by slate flags or quarry tiles. A septic tank was installed in the adjacent field, with real drains that worked! Gradually the internal rooms took shape again, with some changes - an inside bathroom, a bedroom made smaller. Plumbing, electrics, gas and all "mod cons" crept in, we hoped as unobtrusively as possible. When the nine weeks were up, it wasn't finished - but it wasn't far off and we were able to move back in on time. The builders soon completed, leaving us with the clearing up and all the decorating.

Was it worth it? Well yes, in more ways than one. It had cost us a great deal of hard work and money, but now the house was worth more overall than had been spent. Just as important, we now had a home to be proud of and feel a part of, a centrepiece to our smallholding, a haven to return to after a day outside in the elements. We had made some very practical changes too; a sizeable porch at the front door for boots and coats, the back door moved to a new position to give a slate-floored, "wet and muddy" entrance with adjacent washroom; somewhere to hang the waterproofs and clean up before moving into the kitchen. The old solid-fuel range that filled the kitchen with ash every time it was riddled had been replaced with a clean gas-fired equivalent.

Yet for all the undoubted improvements we had made, the house actually looked and felt older, more as it had looked throughout its long life before so much had been hidden away from view in the 1930's. And as a final thought, I had learned a great deal about building work that would stand me in good stead in the future.

Chapter 10
Starting with pigs

We had thought of keeping pigs "one day", at some mythical time in the future when everything else was organised and running smoothly . . . . . but good friends who are a little older and wiser knew that this day would never come, so they hurried things up a bit. As a birthday present I was given a tea chest containing an eight-week-old ginger piglet - a complete surprise. She was pure Tamworth from John and Trudi's own pedigree stock, and I was in at the deep end with enough food for a few days until I could sort things out.

She spent the night in an outbuilding, and the following morning I hastily erected a wire fence to enclose a grass run immediately outside. I wanted to keep her free range like all our other livestock, and at first this arrangement worked very well, with her bedding inside the shelter of the outbuilding plus the grassed area for sunbathing and exercise. Fed twice a day on bought-in feed plus boiled vegetable scraps, she grew fast and responded to attention, becoming very tame and used to being handled. Then one day she pushed her lengthening snout into the soft turf and dug. How cute, we cried, and laughed at her muddy nose; but within a few days she had dug up the whole run, and once bored with that she began to dig up the fence as well.

Our books advised that taut barbed wire at ground level would do the trick. I re-fenced in this fashion and it held, so she dug deeper, turning the run into a bombsite. It was obvious that the winter rains would turn this into a quagmire. If we'd had rough ground to plough up, this could be turned to advantage of course, but we hadn't; it was all permanent pasture that we definitely did not want to disturb. There seemed only two choices: confinement to a pen with a concrete floor, or free ranging with a ringed nose.

So we ringed her. Our friend Bill, an experienced pig-man, showed me how. A noose of strong rope was slipped into her mouth and tightened over the upper jaw, the free end taken over a strong joist in the low-slung outbuilding roof and pulled tight until the pig was held firmly with her head up but weight still on her four feet. Several small copper rings were inserted at intervals around the upper rim of the flat nose, using special pliers made for the purpose. The rings had been sterilised beforehand in boiling water, and an antiseptic wash was applied to the nose before and after their insertion.

It sounds straightforward; but from the moment the rope entered her mouth the pig emitted the most remarkable, high-pitched, ear-piercing continuous squeal with no detectable pause for breath. It took a strong nerve to work calmly under this barrage of sound. When we had finished and removed the rope, she fell silent at once and snuffled happily around as if nothing at all had happened. Naturally her nose was a bit tender for a day or two and she jumped backwards a few times when the new rings touched something solid, but she soon became used to the idea of not forcing her snout into the ground any more. We turned her loose into the Pigs Platt, a half-acre paddock so named on the deeds of our property that led straight off the farmyard, and provided a roomy ark of curved galvanised sheeting on a wooden framework for her sleeping quarters.

Here she grazed happily on the grass, crunched beech mast and other goodies that dropped from the surrounding trees, sunbathed on the muckheap or dozed in the leafy shade as the mood took her. In bad weather she spent more time in her own bed in the dry, but still came out several times a day to graze and exercise. The sight and sounds of Penny the pig (for such was our heroine's name) became very much a part of everyday life on the holding.

It was some weeks later that I began to realise all was not well with Penny. She would suddenly jump back from her food bowl in mid-meal with a squeal, then cautiously approach to continue feeding. I tried other containers for her feed, but over several days it gradually deteriorated until she began to refuse food even on the ground. When a pig refuses food, its serious. Her nose was obviously hurting when feeding, so Bill and I roped her up again for examination, accompanied by the same dreadful squeal. There was no visible sign of any infection or soreness, we just couldn't understand the problem - Bill had never

encountered this before in years of pig keeping. Nevertheless we removed the rings to see what happened. At once she began eating normally again. Problem solved, but we couldn't turn her out again unringed.

Bill suggested a sow ring, a much larger device inserted singly between the two nostrils. No agricultural merchant could provide one, until we were recommended to try an old-established ironmonger in a nearby town. Yes, they had one deep in the archives, in a yellowing packet with the price handwritten upon it in pounds, shillings and pence. Made in much heavier gauge copper, this had a sharpened end for insertion with a hinged section which then swung into place to complete the circle, leaving a smooth, snag-free ring. We fitted this by hand (no special tools required) following much the same restraining and sterilising procedure as before. Once the initial soreness had worn off, this proved to be the answer and Penny wore the ring happily from then on, grazing but not digging to any extent.

Time passed and we began to think about her first litter. We thought it would be nice to breed pure Tamworth, so we began to look for an unrelated boar. Only at this point did we realise how scarce this breed is. We knew it was a rare breed of course, but it turned out to be a long, long way to the nearest pedigree breeder who could offer a boar service. Casting around locally for someone who kept them

in a small way and was perhaps unregistered with the breed society, a friend in the village put us onto just such a person they had known at a previous address. The boar was of pedigree parents but the owner, being interested in producing quality pork rather than pure breeding stock, was unknown outside the locality. No doubt there are many other Tamworths out there in a similar situation; the difficulty lies in finding them.

This one was an hours drive away, and a license was needed to authorise the movement. I called in at the local livestock market to obtain one from the Ministry man there, but of course it wasn't as simple as that. A form had to be completed and signed by both myself and the boar owner before the license could be issued, so I had to fill in my part, post it to the boar owner, wait for its return and then claim my license.

Next came the problem of transport. I had given this some thought and decided that, as my ageing Volvo estate car already moved sheep, building materials, railway sleepers and just about everything else, it could surely cope with the pig as well. A ramp was made from an old door with battens fixed at intervals for grip, and the (t)rusty car parked in the Pigs Platt while Penny was fed morning and evening first at the foot of the ramp, then part-way up, then in the back of the car. She soon learned to scuttle up the ramp after her feeding bowl and became used to being shut in the vehicle for short periods.

When the day came, she walked straight up into the car with no problem at all. It was very amusing watching the reaction of other people to the sight of a large, hairy ginger pig staring out of the side window during the journey over. I had put down a polythene sheet and thick straw bedding, but unlike sheep she did not pass anything until turned out upon arrival.

The boar was a huge fellow, rather overweight and she had some difficulty in standing for him; but she was well in season, he was very keen, and more by luck than judgement they ended up using the side bars of the pen for support while the service took place. After she had rested, it was back in the car again for the return journey. There was so sign of her "repeating" in three weeks time so we began to look forward to her first farrowing.

As the time approached I increased her feed slightly and prepared the farrowing quarters. This was to be one bay of the old stable, with strong wooden partitions, stone walls and cobbled floor. A crush bar (to protect the piglets from being trapped beneath the sow) was fitted along the wooden partition side of the pen, and a galvanised five-barred gate rigged across one end to serve as a creep area with a heat lamp for the piglets. Dried rushes for bedding were chopped into short lengths with garden shears, on Bill's advice, to enable the piglets to move around more easily for their first day or two. A few days before she was due to farrow, I moved her inside to get used to the pen. She moved her bedding to a new position, settled down, and the following day began to farrow. It was a good job I'd brought her in early.

We watched spellbound from a discreet distance as six little piglets arrived over a period of about two hours. It wasn't the biggest litter in the world but they were all perfect and evenly sized, just right for a first-time mother. We hadn't realised before how tiny newborn piglets are, but they were active and keen to suckle right from the start. There didn't seem to be much milk for them, perhaps because of being a few days early, so we gave Penny an injection from the vet to bring on the milk supply.

She hated any of the piglets to touch her face or nose at first as they scuffled around looking for a better teat to suck, and would rear up onto her feet with the danger of injury to her offspring. So we took the piglets away into the safety of their creep under the heat lamp where they would sleep in a contented little pile, and let them through every hour or so to suckle from their mother while one of us was present to guide them away from the head end. This worked very well except that it meant staying up all night. Gradually everything settled down; the milk came in, the piglets were more contented and Penny became used to them snuffling at her face. After forty-eight hours we were able to leave them to it without further interference.

At nine days old the pigs were run outside during the day and brought in for the night (this was late summer). Around five weeks old they were left out the whole time, sharing the ark with their mother. We fed Penny well but even so, by the time her piglets were weaned at eight weeks old she was thin and tired, and showed no signs of regret when we moved her quietly away one morning to enjoy a well-earned rest. The piglets meanwhile had grown at an astonishing rate on their mother's milk plus a gradually increasing diet of dry feed. Once they had settled down to independence, two boars were sold to a friend for fattening, two gilts went to good homes where they would grow on for breeding, and the remaining two boars we kept to fatten for ourselves - one for pork and one for bacon.

Footnote: As with all livestock species, pigs are social animals that need the company of their own kind - but because Penny was a gift, this simply didn't occur to us at the time. Subsequent experience of both friends and ourselves has been that a pet sow, kept in isolation, proves generally difficult to breed from with any consistency. The minimum should be two pigs of similar size and age kept together.

Chapter 11
Pork and bacon

We kept two piglets from our Tamworth sow's first litter to fatten on for pork and bacon. After weaning at eight weeks old, these two were given the run of a fenced-off field corner (about twenty-five yards square) where main crop potatoes had been grown that year and recently lifted. The piglets dug enthusiastically for those tubers missed and for the roots of the inevitable weeds that had grown amongst the crop. I fed them some brought-in nuts and barley plus vegetable scraps as well. For shelter they had an ark of salvaged curved corrugated iron sheeting that I rebuilt onto a framework of scrap timber - free and effective.

The animals grew and gradually the plot became thoroughly ploughed. As the

winter rain began to set in, their constant activity turned the bare earth into a muddy morass until by late November they were up to their armpits in mud. This didn't seem to worry them at all, but it worried me and eventually I moved them indoors to an old outhouse with a dry concrete floor. I left the door open for good ventilation, barring the doorway with a heavy five-bar gate tied into position. Inside, heavy timbers contained an area of deep bedding, the remaining floor area being left bare. The pigs settled in happily, continuing to grow as they devoured steadily increasing rations of food. They chose a dunging corner and provided this was cleaned out about once a week they kept themselves and the rest of their accommodation clean and tidy.

One day I noticed that they had found a weak spot in the concrete floor and begun to excavate with their incredible noses. I didn't think they would get very far - but I was wrong. Over several days they extended the hole outwards until several square yards of concrete had been reduced to rubble fragments. It had been a thin skim of concrete laid straight onto an old beaten-earth floor by the look of it, and once their noses were under it . . . .

By now it was mid-January and both young pigs were showing signs of maturing into boars (this at six months of age), mounting each other, playing more aggressively, and becoming more "pushy" with me and harder to handle at cleaning-out or feeding times. It was time for them to go. At the abattoir, I had a long talk with the butcher who would joint the pigs, explaining that one would be for freezing down as pork, the other for salting into ham and bacon. He took some convincing that I was serious about tackling this at home, but then was most helpful and wrote down my requirements in his book.

In the run-up to this point we had of course researched the subject of home-curing as best as we could. An expert speaker at a smallholding group meeting had extolled the virtues of dry-salted hams above all others; various old farmhouse cookery books listed endless recipes for both dry and wet salting (or brining); friends who kept pigs and had actually done it were interrogated; and of course, *Home Farm* magazine contained information on it! In fact, there seemed so many alternatives that we ended up confused by it all, until our valued friend Richard, with the experience of one pig behind him, summed it all up. He brushed aside our doubts and uncertainties with the calm assurance that there was actually nothing to it, you could chuck in more salt, or less salt, and it would still turn out fine - there was no problem. Imbued with Richard's confidence, I settled for three different strengths of brine solution in which the ham and bacon would be cured, to give us a comparison on which to base future efforts.

The required amounts of salt and saltpetre were obtained, and all was ready - but when I staggered into the kitchen with over two hundred pounds of pig meat to fill the waiting table, Rosie went all weak at the knees and was very little use for the rest of the day! It was, I admit, a daunting prospect, but I set to work wrapping and freezing the pork joints and chops first. Next I made up the three different brine strengths and poured these into home-brew five-gallon bins.

The two sides of bacon were cut into manageable sized pieces and distributed between the three bins of brine. The butcher had already jointed the hams into pieces in line with my request, and with these joints I injected the appropriate brine solution deep into the muscle and especially down beside the bone, before immersion alongside the bacon. The heads and trotters went into a large pan to boil up for brawn, while the remaining poorer cuts of pork were laboriously boned, minced and finally made into sausages. This last operation developed into a family affair around the food mixer with Rosie and I feeding in the minced pork and controlling the flow of skin, while the children, Katie and Martin, twisted the individual sausages and snipped them off ready for freezing. It was a heck of a lot of work for a few pounds of sausages!

Once the brawn and sausages were safely in the freezer, the workload eased considerably. The brine baths were inspected daily and their contents moved around a bit to ensure even treatment of every surface. After the allotted soaking time, each joint of ham was drained and dried off, bagged, labelled and frozen; most of the bacon was sliced up and frozen in packets of half-a-dozen rashers. Two hams and a bacon joint from the strongest brine cure were not frozen but instead were hung in the cool, dark dairy to see how they would keep without any further treatment.

We had eaten Tamworth pork before and been astonished by its flavour, not only of the meat but also of the fat and especially the superb crackling. Our own largely free range, organic pork lived up to this expectation in every way. We used to cut off most of the white, insipid fat from commercial pork and throw it away; now we almost fight over who has the biggest share on their plate, and if the crackling isn't fairly distributed there's a riot! The sausages, being all meat with no "filler" ingredients added, were filling as well as delicious.

As for the ham and bacon, well, it was simply on a different plane to the bland products of the modern supermarket. The hams were tender, succulent and full of flavour hot or cold; the bacon didn't shrink in the frying pan or give off pools of watery liquid, but instead fried crisp and tasty. Older friends and relatives enthused and remarked that they had not experienced such flavours for thirty years or more. Yes, it was worth every minute and every penny that went into it.

The only partial disappointment was the brawn, and that was due to my own lack of culinary skills. With insufficient seasonings added, it was too bland in flavour for most palates, and the unfamiliar texture of small chunks of meat set into firm jelly was not enjoyed by Rosie and the children. I quite liked it actually (perhaps I was prejudiced) and older people did too, again with the association of long-forgotten taste.

The few joints hung up in the dairy kept in good condition for several weeks, the bacon being gradually sliced off as required, but then a film of white mould began to form. It may not have been harmful but I didn't take the chance, and used up or froze the remaining meat. The hams were cooked after the traditional overnight soaking in water, so it perhaps wasn't surprising that the final taste was much the same whichever strength of brine it had originally been cured in. The bacon from the weakest brine bath was just right fried as it was, whereas the stronger brines gave too salty a result for our palates. This was easily remedied by soaking in cold water for twenty to thirty minutes before cooking. With hindsight, it now strikes me as rather pointless to add more salt strength to the brine bath than is necessary for flavour balance if the resulting ham or bacon is to be frozen; really the only purpose of more salt than this is to preserve the meat at air temperature.

For what it is worth, I give the recipes that I used below, but it must be said that my friend Richard was absolutely right - there is nothing to it and the amounts of salt used are not critical.

Weak brine solution (per gallon of water)
8 oz. sugar
8 oz. salt
½ oz. Saltpetre
Soak for one week per pound weight of joint, dry, freeze.

Medium brine solution (per gallon of water)
6 oz. sugar
1 lb. 8 oz. salt
½oz. saltpetre
Soak for four days per pound weight of joint, dry, freeze.

Strong brine solution (per gallon of water)
3 oz. sugar
2 lb. salt
½ oz. saltpetre
Soak for three days per pound weight of joint, dry, hang in cool dark place or freeze.

Footnote: Later experience taught us that rancid flavours could develop in brine-cured meat when the temperature was not cold enough. Professionals keep their brine baths refrigerated. Amateurs can get away with it in an unheated room during cold weather, but its safer to use a large fridge for the purpose, or a deep freeze cabinet rigged up with a thermostat to tick over at just one or two degrees above freezing point.

Chapter 12
Watch out for mink

I was busy at the workshop bench on a lovely morning in early March. The sun was streaming in through the window and the open door, along with all the sounds of springtime; lambs and mothers calling to each other; the native blackbird, thrush, robin, chaffinch and wren all singing to stake their territorial claims before the first of the Summer migrants arrive to swell the morning chorus.

Gradually I became aware of a distant hubbub of scolding and chattering calls from crow and magpie, growing nearer and louder, until suddenly our Aylesbury ducks joined in with their alarm calls. Something was clearly up, and Rosie walked round the corner of the building to look. She called back that a cat-like creature was moving through the shadows of the bushes on the opposite bank of the river.

I quickly joined her and we moved closer to the water, where a mob of scolding birds cackled from the safety of our tall ash trees. Then I saw it, cat-sized but definitely not a cat, moving quickly and sinuously upstream amongst the foliage of the river bank, its fur coat glistening rich chocolate brown in the sunshine. It was a mink, a foreign predator but similar enough perhaps to our own stoat and weasel for the birds to recognise it as a threat. As it crossed open ground, the bolder members among the audience flocked down to "buzz" the intruder, and as it moved away, so they all followed, warning all before them. I followed the mink up to my top boundary to see it safely off the premises, while our ducks settled down again to their leisurely dabbling on the mill pond.

Some of you will have seen mink in or near water. It is often confused with the otter, but there is really no comparison in size. The mink is little larger than a stoat, while an adult otter may exceed four feet in length from nose to tail tip. The mink is both feared and hated as a vicious predator of fish, game and poultry, while a folklore of horror stories surrounds the animal. What are the facts?

A scientific paper details a study of feral mink in specific areas of South Devon. Live trapping, tagging and release work combined with radio tracking gave some interesting results over a two-year period. Mink are solitary animals, resident in an area (territory), the size of which is dependent upon the prey available - around two kilometres of bank in the relatively poor habitat of a moorland river, down to half a kilometre in the rich habitat of an unspoilt shallow coastline. The animal moves regularly between its upper and lower boundaries, never far from the water's edge, feeding and resting in dens as it goes, returning to its starting point over a four to seven day cycle.

In addition to these residents there are "transient" mink that travel through in two "waves" each year. The first wave, from January to March, comprises adult males looking for potential mates; the second wave, from August to October, comprises juveniles dispersing from their mothers' territory. Outside of these periods hardly any travelling animals are encountered.

Many attempts have been made to control the numbers of mink by man, largely without success. The study was able to examine two of these control attempts. The landowner of a short stretch of river carried out a relentless campaign of trapping and shooting, killing more than one hundred animals over a five year period. During the two years of the study he killed thirty-four, all during the two waves of transient animals with none during the remaining six months of the year. At the end of it all there was still one resident mink including his stretch within its territory, as there had been at the beginning.

The Devon and Cornwall minkhounds hunt the two counties (they were formerly the Devon and Cornwall otterhounds, but when the otter became protected by law they changed their name and quarry and carried on much as before). They hunted once during the study period over the ground being studied, killing one resident out of six animals known to live there. Their hunting records showed a total of eighty-four mink killed over the previous five years. The study concluded that hunting had an insignificant effect upon mink numbers, and that trapping/shooting campaigns are rendered ineffective by the twice-yearly waves of transient animals which quickly settle into a vacant territory should the resident be removed.

Little is known of the eventual fate of the transient mink, in particular the autumn wave of juveniles. It is presumed that those animals which have not found a vacant or other suitable territory for themselves before the onset of winter must perish, otherwise they would continue to be trapped in studies such as this. So, in common with all other successful predators, the mink has a sophisticated control mechanism to ensure that numbers are limited by the prey available, and that individuals removed from this balance are quickly replaced. It seems that the mink is here to stay, an established predator filling to a certain extent the vacant niche left by the decline of the otter.

The animal travelling our stretch of river in March was very probably an adult male in search of a potential mate. The speed of his passage may have indicated that he found no female scent here, which in turn may indicate that we have no resident mink. I have found evidence of them from time to time by way of footprints and droppings, but these may have been transients and our free range hens and ducks, very tempting prey to a resident animal, had remained unharmed.

It was late summer when mink were brought sharply back to our attention. A grey overcast day of squally showers kept us working indoors instead of outside, while the wind noise in the trees and around the buildings isolated us from the familiar sounds of the holding. After tea, we put on waterproofs to set out on the round of livestock. Rosie soon returned looking puzzled from the orchard behind the mill; there were no ducks waiting at the gate eager for their food as usual, and none to be seen in their favourite haunts either.

Once the other jobs were finished I went to investigate, already sensing that something was seriously wrong. Down at the river bank lay the evidence to confirm this - white feathers trampled in the soft mud, some stained with blood; a trail of clues down to the water itself. No fox could squeeze under that particular place in the wire fence, nor would he take his kill to water given a choice.

I fetched my waders and entered the water, to work slowly down the margin looking for further evidence. Fifty yards downstream the bank is hollowed out behind an old tree stump, and here I found more white down feathers trampled in the mud, over-printed by mink tracks. Perhaps one bird had been partly eaten here, but there was no carcase or any other signs to be found despite careful searching upstream and down. Our two Aylesbury ducks and their drake had gone for good.

I found it surprising that a small animal such as the mink would kill and carry off in turn three birds weighing more than twice his own bodyweight. And why in broad daylight? They are nocturnal hunters. Perhaps the very unseasonal wild wet weather was a part of the answer; certainly it had hidden from our ears the alarm calls and commotion which on most normal days would have alerted us to what was happening.

With other poultry to protect I set a cage trap at the river margin, partly covered with undergrowth and baited with a fish based cat food that mink apparently find attractive. Of course I didn't expect the culprit to be hungry straightaway, with three ducks salted away somewhere, so I ran the trap for ten days, checking at least twice daily. Throughout this time I carefully checked the riverbank for prints or droppings, but saw nothing to indicate the continued presence of mink. The trap was finally sprung on the tenth day. I could see that the door was snapped shut as I approached, and something dark was moving around in the shady interior of the cage. With the legendary fierceness of the cornered mink very much in mind, I cautiously pulled back the covering of vegetation to reveal my capture. It was the local moorhen: so they like cat food too!

I opened the cage door to release him unharmed, and was amused to find him foraging in the same spot the very next day. I had put away the trap by then, and we have not been bothered by mink again; it seemed to be an isolated animal travelling through.

Living as we do beside the river, we have to accept that the watercourse is going to be used as a highway by mink on the move; but apart from that one exception it seems sufficient protection to shut away our free range poultry before darkness falls and let them out again in the morning light.

Chapter 13
Building the sheep flock

The tale has been told in previous chapters of our sheep apprenticeship with Bill's flock. Seven months after moving into our smallholding, we purchased our first breeding stock.

Unlike most commercial farmers, our primary interest lay in the fleece and its suitability for hand spinning. Rosie came to know a local spinner and weaver who kept her own small flock of crossbred ewes for the same reason, and we chose one of her yearlings with well-grown single ewe lamb at heel to begin our flock. The ewe, Matilda, was a mixture of Lincoln Longwool, Jacob and black Shetland, and being a lamb herself the previous year, had never been shorn; her fleece was rich chocolate brown, lustrous and nicely crimped - a hand spinner's dream. Bill sheared her for us to yield ten pounds of wool. The lamb, Harriet, had Black Leicester Longwool influence from the sire and carried a similar, but finer, fleece to her mother.

The arrival of these very dark-coloured sheep caused a bit of a stir in the village, and before we knew it Bill himself had bought two coloured ewes with lambs at market. These were Suffolks crossed with another unknown breed to give a dense, short-stapled wool of mid-brown colour, not an ideal hand spinner's fleece, but to Bill they were the right colour for us! He kindly gave us one of the ewe lambs after weaning, which we christened Chocolate for the obvious reason.

Then word reached us that a local farmer had taken some fat lambs to market and brought one back home, rejected by the grader for being too fat. It was a coloured ewe lamb; were we interested? We called round one evening to see it and the old farmer led us to a field where a narrow neck opened out into unseen acres beyond. He spoke two words to his dog, which ran off out of sight, and there we stood for quite some time, chatting away, until eventually we heard the sound of hooves approaching. The sheep flock raced around the corner of the hedge into the narrow neck of the field and right up to the gate, closely followed by the dog who penned them tightly there, then dropped to the ground - all this without any further command from his master. We were able to examine the lamb concerned, another Suffolk-cross type animal but with softer, finer wool than Chocolate had. And so she joined our little band and was named Coffee after her colour.

By now it was August and the local group of the Rare Breeds Survival Trust had organised a sale at Exeter jointly with the Coloured Sheep Breeders' Association. A fascinating day spent looking at rare breeds and primitive sheep saw the Volvo estate car speeding homewards with three more sheep on board (to think that this used to be my posh executive car!). These were a pedigree Shetland yearling ewe, smokey grey and named Crystal; her ewe lamb to a Jacob sire, almost black so we called her Jet; and last but by no means least, a pedigree Shetland ewe lamb, oatmeal fleeced with striking black and white "badger" face markings. This last animal was knocked down to me by the auctioneer long after I had dropped out of the bidding, or so I had thought; apparently Rosie was still smiling at him over my shoulder! With a mother named Dormouse, the children chose her name as Doormat and, unflattering though this was, it stuck

With tupping time approaching we gave some thought to the question of a suitable ram, and decided to split our little flock two ways. It would be nice to breed the Shetlands pure, and fortunately a breeder in the next village agreed to accept Crystal and Doormat for a few weeks for service by his pedigree ram lamb. Jet was too small to be included in this. For the others, Rosie fancied some Gotland influence, so a suitable ram lamb was located for hire and we drove one hour to collect him, only to be told on arrival that he was just developing symptoms of orf, an unpleasant and highly infectious viral condition. Our flock was believed free of this disease so we decided not to use this ram after all.

The lady who had sold us our first sheep came to the rescue and took Matilda, Chocolate and Coffee for service by her Black Leicester Longwool x Jacob ram. Thus we now had no sheep on the place, and much time was spent driving around checking on our ewes elsewhere. This was far from ideal and we resolved to bring the ram to us next time.

While this was going on an advertisement in the local paper revealed a small flock of ten Jacobs being sold off. We called to inspect and selected three ewes with the best fleeces. These had been with a Jacob ram for some weeks and so were presumed already in-lamb for the first time, not having been put to the ram the previous year. These were christened by our children as Smudge (because of her face markings), Fudge (because of her colour), and Smidge (because it almost, sort of, rhymed) - ah well, don't blame me!

By Christmas all animals were back on our grass, with hay fed ad-lib. Lambing was due to start, in theory, at Easter and we began trough feeding of concentrates six weeks before this, gradually building up to around one pound per head per day. As this extra feeding started, the opportunity was offered by a local farmer to pregnancy scan our sheep by ultrasonic means - all we had to do was transport ours over to his place while the contractor was working through his own flock. More out of interest than need, we took up the offer, wrote down the contractor's assessment of the number of lambs carried by each animal, and returned them to their field.

Nine days later I found Doormat laying in the grass showing every sign of trying to give birth, but this should be four or five weeks away. The vet confirmed that she was trying to abort a dead lamb and removed the offending foetus, a sad start to our lambing. Stress is often blamed for such abortion in first-time mothers, and the only stress she'd had was the scanning.

The rest of the flock jogged along nicely, swelling by the day. With one week to go we began to bring them in at night, bedded down under electric light where we could check throughout the hours of darkness. On Easter Day itself, we sat sharing a welcome mug of hot tea in the kitchen with Bill after all the morning rounds had been attended to, when there came a knock on the door. It was John, our neighbouring farmer across the river - did we know that one of our ewes had lambed right by the water's edge? He'd noticed them while checking his own stock. We'd only checked them less than an hour before, but we all trooped down the field and sure enough there was one of the Jacobs, Smudge, proudly licking twins; both ewe lambs too! I carried them back to dry off under a heat lamp in the comfort of a strawed pen. Our very own lambs, what a great feeling.

We stepped up the watches, day and night. Chocolate was next to lamb, indoors this time. The scanner had told us to be careful not to overfeed as she was carrying a big single; in fact she gave birth to very small twins - so small and weak that they were unable to suckle effectively by themselves. Their mother, being inexperienced, simply wouldn't stand still long enough for these little scraps to find the teat. We assisted for the first thirty-six hours by restraining the mother and teaching the lambs to suck until they all had the hang of it. We had chosen not to take the scanner's advice and fed Chocolate the same as our other ewes, rather than cutting down as he had suggested because of the "big single" - just as well, as it turned out. This experience on top of Dormat's abortion led us to decide that scanning was not for us again.

The lambs followed on nicely from there, all born without assistance from us and some in the daytime which allowed our two children to watch along with us (it was the Easter holidays). The last lamb caused our only problem. Coffee, the Suffolk cross, produced a large head with one foot only showing beneath it, and was unable to progress any further. I had helped Bill to deal with this situation before, so I had the confidence to grasp the one leg firmly, pull as the ewe strained and ease the shoulders through to deliver a very large ram lamb safely.

The final count was eleven lambs to seven ewes, not bad considering that most were first-time mothers - and it had happened in fifteen days from start to finish, after using three different rams! Beginners' luck no doubt, but it was a

most enjoyable and rewarding time for us all. The flock made a fine sight in the spring sunshine, the ewes grazing or resting while their lambs sprang, raced and tumbled around with the energy of young lives.

We fed the ewes concentrates for a further four weeks, tapering off as the rising protein value of the May grass took over. The flock was housed overnight for two weeks after lambing, to prevent losses to predators (especially foxes) or to inclement weather. They all did well under this system. In the fullness of time, we selected five ewe lambs to grow on and join our breeding flock, four wethers (castrated males) were sold to friends who wanted lawnmowers on legs, and the remaining two graced the inside of our deep freeze. I had thought that it was going to be a problem persuading Rosie and the children to eat our own lamb, but once they had tasted that first meal, all resistance faded away......

Chapter 14
Sheep skills

Following a year's apprenticeship with Bill's sheep flock, we began to acquire our own breeding stock and lambed them for the first time as already described. At the same time we attended short courses on sheep handling and management, and read books and magazine articles on these subjects. There seemed an awful lot to learn - but actually putting it into practice was less daunting than it had first seemed. Then we learned a few things we hadn't found in books . . . .

Initially we were taught foot trimming using a pocketknife. It was some time before I discovered foot shears, which are safer (for both sheep and handler) and more effective, enabling more accurate, controlled cutting. Now the knife is reserved for emergencies only.

It was some time too, before I discovered the sheep seat or chair, which takes much of the backache out of foot trimming; these hook over a hurdle or gate to present a sheep-sized deck chair into which the animal can be reversed and the front legs lifted into a sitting position. Most sheep will sit happily in one of these while their feet are attended to, though a restraining strap across the chest is necessary for the awkward customers.

One day, Bill came back from market with ten very large Suffolk-type ewes he had bought. Together we checked them over and found that their feet had been badly neglected, with horn overgrowth concealing large pockets of black rotting tissue. We trimmed, sprayed, and then put them in with the rest of his flock. Within a very short time the other, previously clear ewes began showing signs of lameness. Examination showed foot rot spreading through the flock, from pockets of infection still present in the ten new animals despite our initial treatment. It took a great deal of time and effort to eliminate foot rot from the whole flock by frequent trimming and spraying of every affected foot, and moving to fresh ground to avoid reinfection. Disinfection of the foot shears between each animal handled seemed to help. Of course, what we should have done was to isolate the ten ewes and eliminate the problem before mixing them with the rest; it was a hard-learned lesson.

Bill did not possess a drenching gun, so used a syringe with no needle to dispense worming compounds into the mouths of his ewes. At least this was accurate, but for more than a handful of sheep it was fiddly and time-consuming. I found a drenching gun in one of the boxes of odds and ends at a farm sale, and bought it very cheaply. This proved much quicker and easier to use when the whole flock needed dosing. But there is more to this drenching business than meets the eye. There are wormers and there are wormers! Some are only effective against certain parasites, and furthermore, they are not as one hundred percent effective as we are led to believe. This was brought dramatically home to us by the tapeworm episode.

It was Rosie who first drew our attention to the white, ribbon-like segments in the fresh droppings of Bill's lambs - the classic symptom of tapeworm infestation. We read the small print on the wormer that Bill had been routinely using to learn that it was ineffective against tapeworm, so he bought a different one from the vet which would do the trick. The result of dosing with this was dramatic, when long whitish ribbons poured out of the lambs after a few hours. All very impressive, but being a sceptic I kept a watchful eye on the droppings and within a fortnight the tell-tale segments were back again. The small print on the drench claimed effectiveness against tapeworm segments, which sounds fine but wait a minute - don't tapeworms have heads and bodies as well? Indeed they do, and careful study of yet more small print on other packaging revealed that some wormers (surprisingly few) would kill the heads as well as segments.

One such worm drench was administered, twice at a short interval with a move to fresh ground, and the problem disappeared for that year; but every year since, tapeworm has crept in sooner or later among the lambs and although the right drench checks it back to harmless proportions, we can never quite eliminate it. At least you can see tapeworms; most sheep worm eggs are invisible to the naked eye and the shepherd sees only the symptoms of infection in the affected animal. I feel sure that the same principle applies to all wormers, in that one hundred percent kill of internal parasites is rarely achieved in practice.

Bill's ten ewes that had brought in the foot rot taught us another lesson when they lambed. Several lambs, born apparently strong and healthy, suddenly sickened and died one after another. The vet diagnosed lamb dysentery, one of the clostridial diseases that Bill had vaccinated his flock against, but these ten ewes had only received his annual booster injection four weeks before lambing, along with the rest of the flock.

He later learned (too late) that these ewes had never been under a system of clostridial protection with their previous owner, and so needed two initial injections several weeks apart to set up the necessary antibodies in their blood-streams. Ever since then we have been careful to check the clostridial protection status of any sheep bought in to our own flock, and in case of any doubt to give the two initial injections anyway. The miserable deaths of those wretched lambs were avoidable and this presents a dilemma to those flock owners who wish to register with the Soil Association as organic lamb producers, for their standard states that the use of clostridial vaccine is restricted to "known farm problem".

There are different opinions on this issue, but we see nothing wrong with the principle of protective vaccination to prevent suffering and death by the promotion of natural antibodies. We are not prepared to expose our livestock to this unnecessary risk, any more than we would deny our own children the protection they receive against whooping cough, diphtheria, polio and tetanus at an early age.

So we vaccinate, but I have found the clostridial injection difficult to administer in practice. It has to be subcutaneous (just under the skin) to be effective, and a tip from a *Home Farm* article was to lift a pinch of neck wool between finger and thumb, pulling a flap of skin up along with it. The needle can then go into this raised "tent" of skin at a shallow angle (i.e. nearly parallel with the body) to administer the dose correctly. It still needs careful judgement though. If the needle goes in too deep, the vaccine squirts out the other side; too shallow and it squirts back out of the hole made by the needle; but with care it can be done.

At tupping time, Bill would smear a paste of raddle powder mixed with oil onto the ram's chest so that the ewes were marked in turn as they were served. He warned me against using a ram harness, which he had found in the past to chafe the ram until the animal was too sore to continue serving. Checking the flock twice daily, I soon noticed that it was obvious which ewe was the centre of the ram's attentions because they were standing together whispering sweet sheepy nothings to each other . . . . so with our own small flock, we now simply put in the ram and watch two or three times a day, noting in a diary the date that each ewe comes into season. The lambs duly follow in pretty much the same order; it's easy and there's no messy colour marking of the fleeces.

Visitors often express surprise that we manage without a sheepdog, but we do manage, and very well most of the time, with a food bucket. The ewes soon learn whilst being trough-fed prior to lambing, and if you then keep them interested with a few tit-bits here and there through the rest of the year, they will follow that bucket anywhere. We must admit though to one failure, a group of four animals which came from a larger, non-bucket trained flock, and which have remained wary and difficult to handle; they just seem to be highly-strung and we are now considering selling them because they are simply too much trouble all round - not just in the matter of the food bucket.

Dipping is hard work for us and stressful for the sheep, but it does have its compensations. We are fortunate to have a neighbour with his own dip just up the road, and there is a certain twisted pleasure in holding up the traffic while we drive our flock up the hill, past the church and along a bit further to the farm entrance - especially the lorries. Also it is one of the few times in a year when we work alongside our neighbours, catching up on each other's news, a social occasion really. Now that we have our own rams I take them up separately in a small trailer behind the car, and if our neighbours were astonished to see these follow the food bucket to the brink of the dip, you should have seen their faces when the soaking animals followed meekly all the way back to the trailer again afterwards!

At shearing time, most people call in the contractors, but I wanted to do it myself if possible. After some searching I picked up an old bench-mounted electric shearing set, with a narrower comb and cutter to the handpiece than the modern equipment, for £30. With a little maintenance this proved to be in working order and I was ready to try my hand. I'd had no training, and though I'd seen it done a few times, I had no illusions that it would be easy.

It wasn't. The first attempts were a real struggle, though I did manage to remove the fleece (eventually) without removing anything else belonging to the sheep. The main thing is to hold the animal correctly; the skin must be tight for loose folds of skin will cut, and the shorn fleece should fall cleanly away by gravity at each stroke or you cannot see where you are cutting next. But knowing these principles and achieving them on a struggling sheep are two different matters. Gradually I have developed a style of sorts that suits me, even if it would make a professional wince. It takes me quite a long time to remove a fleece, but with relatively few sheep to shear, the time taken is not really important and I can I concentrate on doing a good job. Few livestock tasks are more satisfying than passing the clippers over a ewe of our own breeding, the warm fleece falling steadily away in gleaming folds, - our hand spinning harvest for the annual shepherding cycle.

Footnote: Dipping against sheep scab is no longer compulsory, is stressful for the animals, involves the use of potentially harmful chemicals, and should not be necessary in a closed flock anyway - so these days we don't do it. Sheep scab has never been an issue here. Fly strike (the laying of eggs in the wool that develop into burrowing maggots) was also controlled by dipping and remains a threat to sheep everywhere; we counter this by applying an organically approved pour-on chemical to the fleece before the high-risk period of warm summer weather.

Clostridial vaccination is another precaution that becomes unnecessary once a closed flock has become established - that is, replacements are home bred so that no sheep are bought in from outside. We stopped using the vaccine several years ago and have experienced no problems so far.

Chapter 15
An experience with orf

If our first lambing had gone like a dream (see chapter 13) then our second lambing turned into a nightmare.

It had started well enough. We hired a ram and brought him to our ewes, thus avoiding all the chasing around of the previous year when the ewes had gone away to different rams. One of the Jacob ewes developed a prolapsed cervix as lambing time approached, but I was able to replace this and used a T-shaped plastic retainer to keep it in place. It turned out that this was the only ewe that caused us to call in the vet at lambing; she strained for ages without making any progress, and on examination I found that the neck of the cervix was not fully dilated, such that I was unable to pass my hand through.

Afraid to force the issue, I called out the vet in the small hours of the morning. He said that prolapsed cases were often "tight", shoved his hand through and whipped out healthy twin lambs. It was all a matter of confidence really; I resolved to cope on my own next time. And I did cope with our first breech presentation, when the ewe strained away until a solitary tail appeared with no feet in sight. Gently replacing the lamb into the womb to sort things out, my fingers found a

tangle of legs - too many for twins! Keeping hold of the tail, I followed the textbook instructions and felt around the hindquarters to draw back first one leg, then the other, before delivering the lamb backwards. Two more lambs quickly followed to give us healthy triplets, a very satisfying result

There were no other problems really and we finished with twenty-two lambs from ten ewes, all in nine days flat. Results like these imply good flock management and we were feeling very pleased with ourselves - but this was soon to change.

Bill was using some of our grazing for his own small flock, which had lambed a few weeks before our own. One of his lambs had developed a sore mouth and I helped him to pen them for examination. He was puzzled to find scabs on the outer lip only, with no soreness inside the mouth. Whatever it was, he said, it wasn't orf. Now it so happened that by a most unfortunate coincidence, I suspected that one of our own ewes had developed mastitis and I wanted the benefit of Bill's experience - so without thinking of the possible consequences I asked him to look at her. This he did, without disinfecting his hands first; then, as he handled the inflamed udder, the stupidity of my request hit me, too late.

It was mastitis but confined to one side of the udder, so her twin lambs were able to continue feeding from the other side while a course of injections was given. Over a period of several days the mastitis subsided, but it failed to clear completely and no more milk came in on that side. More days passed until my daily inspection of her twin lambs revealed the signs I didn't want to see; swollen and bleeding gums around the teeth, while the ewe's udder was suddenly inflamed again with infection. The vet confirmed that this was orf. He treated the ewe with more powerful antibiotics, and the lambs with anthiomaline (containing antimony) for injection plus terramycin aerosol for spraying directly onto the open sores. Neither of these would cure orf, but they would ease the symptoms.

The condition of both ewe and lambs deteriorated fast until we were forced to separate them, bottle-feeding the lambs in a pen alongside their mother. It was a grim business persuading them to suck with raw, bleeding mouths but once they were hungry enough, they managed somehow. Within a few days the orf symptoms began to appear in other lambs of our flock. Despite twice-daily inspection and isolation of the affected animals at the first signs, it slowly and inexorably spread. Ewes developed scabs and then open sores on the teats and around the udder to compound the misery, with mother and young both in pain when suckling. The treatments seemed to have little effect.

Word soon spread in our small community of the "luer" outbreak, this being the local name for orf. Neighbours were sympathetic and gave what advice they could. John, across the river, gave me a tub of udder cream that he used on his dairy cows. This he suggested applying twice daily to the teats and udder of affected ewes, keeping the skin softer and less liable to split and develop sores. It certainly helped and was sound advice. Even so, I would prefer to forget the next three weeks, with each morning and evening a marathon session of medication, spraying, injecting, rubbing in cream, hand-milking some ewes too sore to suckle then persuading their equally sore offspring to drink it from a bottle. And I felt personally responsible for starting this miserable cycle.

Several people recommended charming against orf, and had known it to work. Rosie leans more to this kind of thing than me, and in desperation approached a person credited with the ability to charm away orf. She was assured that we could stop treating it now, and that it would go away within a few days. We didn't stop the treatment and it didn't go away.

But gradually it ran its course and those animals first affected began to heal and clear. In time this followed through the flock, although against the flow of improvement there was one surprise infection - me. The backs of both hands and wrists broke out in a rash of raised, itching red lumps, not painful, just irritating. I was packed off to the doctors where I explained that I'd been handling orf-infected sheep for the past few weeks (I knew that it was transferable to humans). He said it wasn't orf, probably an allergic reaction to a chemical I'd been handling. We don't use chemicals so this wasn't much help. Fortunately the rash faded away of its own accord within a few days.

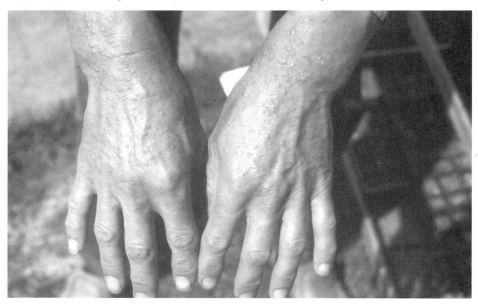

One month after the outbreak had started, it was all over. We hadn't lost any animals, but only because our relatively small numbers enabled us to give the close attention which would be impossible in a large flock. We were physically and emotionally drained by the end. A particular irony was that Bill's lamb with the original mouth sores healed up quickly, while no others in his flock were affected. With hindsight, I wondered whether this first infection had been orf at all, or did our own ewe start the outbreak with her mastitis? We will never know.

There remained the prospect of a repeat outbreak the following year. The orf virus is known to persist on a farm for several years once introduced, being susceptible to frost on the open ground but often over wintering in dirty outbuildings or sheltered hedge bottoms. I set to work disinfecting the buildings, hurdles, feed troughs, hayracks and anything else inside which the infected animals had made contact with. As luck would have it, there was bitter cold spell of hard frosts during the following winter that should have killed off any pockets of infection outside. Should we hope that this was sufficient, or should we vaccinate against orf?

Some local farmers swore by the vaccine; they still had orf symptoms at times in the flock, but on a much milder scale so as to cause few problems. But it is a live vaccine and its use seems a permanent commitment to continue using it. John, my neighbour on the uphill side, told me of a similar miserable outbreak of malignant orf he'd suffered one year in a much bigger flock than ours. The vaccine was just becoming widely available and he had debated whether or not to use it. In the end he didn't, yet the following lambing was completely clear of orf - and as he put it, if he had vaccinated he'd have sworn it was wonderful stuff.

We decided against vaccination. There was no orf the following year, nor the year after; we sincerely hope that it stays that way.

Chapter 16
Visitors

When we moved a distance of two hundred and fifty miles to start a new direction in life on our smallholding, we didn't really expect to see many visitors. Wrong! Little did we know how many friends, relatives, ex-neighbours, ex-workmates and ex-acquaintances would descend upon us within the next couple of years.

Of course it was a great pleasure to see them at first, to share our euphoria with them, to keep in touch with the old life through them, to show what we had done and what we planned to do. But as our first summer came and the flow of visitors became a flood, the realisation dawned that these people we were delighted to see individually were creating an unforeseen problem collectively. It seemed churlish to complain - but consider the facts.

Having travelled a long way to see us, visitors needed to relax, to eat and drink, often to sleep for one or more nights. So the vegetables, fruit, eggs and meat that we worked hard to produce, and that were the mainstay of our lifestyle on a smaller income, were increasingly consumed by other people. But of far greater significance was the amount they consumed of that most valuable of commodities - time. It took time to welcome visitors, refresh them, then show them around the land, the buildings, the livestock, the locality; and while we were doing this, we weren't progressing with the long list of jobs which waited to be tackled. And they had to be tackled if our smallholding was to be viable. One or two days "off" a week we could manage, but not every day of the week when the visitors were coming thick and fast. A further complication was that we had no spare bedroom for overnight guests, so there was a good deal of reshuffling of sleeping arrangements, and long queues for the bathroom.

It was all largely our own fault. We had moved to a holiday area, in a quiet corner it's true, but not too far off the main tourist routes, so naturally it was very easy for people to combine their annual break with a visit to us by means of a modest diversion. And we had issued invitations to visit like confetti at a wedding - all sincerely meant at the time, but never seriously believing that so many people would take up the offer. Another factor was the genuine interest in what we were now doing; it seemed that many town-dwellers harboured a dream to move back to the country "one day", and were keen to see if we could make it work.

Somehow we managed through that first summer, and as the children returned to school and the visitor flood waned, we vowed to handle the situation in a different manner the following year. It seemed like a good idea to spread things out so we encouraged visitors around Easter. "Come when we're lambing" we said, "you'll love it". Some did come and they did love it, while we were really pleased to see them. Even so, to our own surprise we found it very tiring indeed combining hospitality with sleepless nights plus the considerable extra workload of lambing. So that wasn't the answer.

Encouraging friends to camp or caravan during the warmer months, rather than cramming into the house with us, has worked well on the whole. Both visitors and ourselves are more independent of each other, a long stay does not represent any drain on our resources, and we can enjoy each others company at times while continuing to cope with the seasonal workload. Friends who regularly stay are more aware of what needs doing and are often only too pleased to help if they can; indeed working on the holding becomes an integral part of their holiday, a complete change from their normal routine.

We can genuinely welcome visitors to the house during the winter months, during periods of lighter workload. There's still plenty to do, but most of it can wait a few days at that time of the year. Best of all are those people who make cups of tea, scrub the potatoes for lunch or set the table without being asked; they become a part of the household and help it to cope with the extra numbers.

There are some very positive aspects to the visitor "problem". Showing someone around the holding for the first time refreshes our perspective of how fortunate we are to live here in the way we do; or a return visit draws into sharp focus all the things we have achieved since their previous call. Familiarity can sometimes mask our own awareness of these things, but the fresh eyes of the visitor bring a renewed perception to our own. Working visitors can be a real help, easing the load at peak times or reducing a near-impossible task to a manageable amount when shared. One year I had strained an arm turning the muck-heap, and was unable to do very much at all for a fortnight, right in the peak holiday season. Friends who were camping and caravanning rallied around to work under my direction at fencing, livestock tasks and tractor driving to keep things moving - we could not have managed without them.

I know I am sticking my neck out writing this piece because some of our visitors will probably read it! But there is no offence intended, and if I am to address the whole experience of a new lifestyle in smallholding, the subject of visitors could not truthfully be ignored. We know from our many new friends in smallholding that the visitor problem is widespread and that there is no simple solution; perhaps the nearest thing to an ideal arrangement is letting your holiday self-catering accommodation to visitors at the normal commercial rate. We're told that even this presents problems - but it makes you wonder about that old barn across the yard . . . .

Chapter 17
Minimum dig vegetables

I have already mentioned the allotment-sized vegetable garden of heavy soil overlying clay. My predecessor here had been a rotovator-and-artificial-fertiliser man, and had practised no crop rotation. Low down in the river valley, the garden would be in a frost pocket and suffer poor drainage. I marked out the plot into beds four feet wide aligned north-south, with paths between which were alternately eighteen and twenty-four inches wide for foot and wheelbarrow access respectively. These beds were neither raised nor deeply dug, but simply not walked upon.

At first there was a heavy weed infestation (thanks to the rotovator) that was laboriously cleared by hand. The paths needed weeding too; I tried hoeing them, which was far quicker than hand weeding but it soon became a chore. Cinders from the coal-fired range smothered the weeds and gave a firmer surface to the path - but soon enough the weeds grew through again and then couldn't be hoed.

As our sheep flock grew, so did the muckheap comprising the soiled soft rush bedding from the lambing houses, plus contributions from the hens, ducks and pigs. Piled in a convenient field corner and left for six months or so, this gave fibrous, part-rotted manure for use in the garden.

Working with six beds initially, I planned out a six-year crop rotation and began a diary to keep track of things. At first I trenched in the manure for the heavy-feeding crops such as early potatoes, broad and runner beans, and sweetcorn, so that as these crops moved around the garden the whole plot would be eventually be fed. This represented a good deal of digging and the weeding still needed doing.

Looking for ways to ease the workload, I tried mulching the paths with a covering of old carpet. This took a little time and effort to lay, but once in place proved very effective at weed suppression. With no bed-edging to work to, I made a vertical cut using a spade and pressed two or three inches of carpet into this, again with the spade, before firming back the soil. This held the carpet strips firmly in place against winter gales. Both hessian and foam-backed carpets were used, pattern-up or backing-up, to see how they compared. Naturally this gave rise to plenty of leg pulling, as we had no carpets in the house at this stage!

On the beds themselves I spread manure in a mulch several inches thick during the autumn as crops were cleared. This killed virtually all weeds over the winter, while the worms multiplied and aerated the soil beneath with their burrows. In the spring, I found that some crops could be sown straight into or

through the undisturbed mulch layer, which meant no weeds through the summer either. Small seeds were sown after removal of the mulch with minimum cultivation of the soil surface to discourage weed germination.

Overall this system gave a lot less work in terms of digging and weeding, so I have persevered with it. I'm no expert, nor even an enthusiastic gardener; all I am looking for is to remain largely self-sufficient in organic vegetables for the least amount of work - and this is what I have found so far.

Potatoes can be dibbered through the mulch at planting time to the soil level beneath. No earthing-up is required. There is some wastage through the development of green tubers at the surface, but it's still a worthwhile crop and for very little work. Easier still is to press the seed potatoes into the mulch surface before covering with a thick layer of spoiled hay. The haulm soon pushes up through the hay to develop as normal, and at harvest you simply draw aside the remaining hay to pick up the crop - no digging required! Again some of the tubers will be green if light has penetrated anywhere.

Young plants raised in the seedbed or greenhouse are trowelled into the mulch surface, just as they would be planted in the soil; these include sweetcorn, outdoor tomato, lettuce, courgette, celeriac, leek, cabbage, sprouts and broccoli. Onion sets are pressed straight in. The large seeds of legumes are dibbered straight through the mulch - broad, runner and french beans, and peas.

The only real problem I have had with any of the above is an increase in slug damage (and it's bad enough here anyway). The mulch layer encourages these pests and gives rise to more damage than growing in bare soil. I haven't found the complete answer to this but transplanting good-sized, sturdy plants is more than half the battle, as they very quickly outgrow any damage. Salt barriers around emerging seedlings are quite effective too, but only in dry weather. Predators are encouraged and the garden is host to hedgehogs, slowworms, frogs, toads, lizards and more besides - but there still seem to be plenty of slugs to go round.

Small seeds present more of a challenge as they cannot be sown directly into the mulch; these include lettuce along with most roots such as carrot, parsnip, turnip, beetroot, and radish. Some of the methods I have tried are as follows:

• Remove the remaining mulch shortly before sowing time, then employ minimum cultivation (just a light raking to produce the necessary soil structure) before sowing. This is not as straightforward as it sounds, because the soil beneath the mulch layer is wetter than bare earth and it hasn't been dug or frosted, so it's not easy to work into a fine tilth. It's best to rake two or three times with a few days in between, so that the soil dries out and crumbles down gradually. This, and moving the mulch layer away, is all extra work - but it does give results and with very little weed competition.

• Lightly dig in the remains of the mulch to the top few inches of soil before working to a tilth for sowing. This suffers the same disadvantages as the first method, and the cure is the same too - several rakings over a period to dry out and break down the soil to a suitable structure.

• Leaving the mulch in place, form shallow drills in its surface and partly fill these with compost or fine soil. Sow the seed on this and cover with more compost or soil to the desired depth. Again, this is not as straightforward as it sounds; taking out drills in fibrous, part-rotted mulch is not easy, and slug damage can be heavy to emerging seedlings. On the credit side, it's quick to do and there is rapid growth once plants are established.

• The best option, but not always possible - when the mulch has been down for a previous season's crop, so is then eighteen months old, the remainder is a fine dark friable tilth just right for direct sowing. There is minimum work involved and slug damage is back to normal levels, though annual weeds will now germinate to compete and it may not suit your crop rotation to leave the mulch intact for so long. But where it is possible, it works well.

Back on the paths, time has shown that the cheapest synthetic-pile, foam-backed carpets laid right side up have lasted the longest - still largely weed free after four years. The patterns and colours dull down after a while so that the paths look better. Laid wrong way up, the foam backing breaks up gradually until weeds can penetrate. Traditional hessian backing and wool pile rots away after a couple of seasons.

I am now trialling heavy gauge black polythene (old silage bags or sheets are free) on some paths, and so far it has stood up well to both weather and wear. Polythene is more easily damaged than carpet to allow weeds to grow through, but against this it does not trap any soil on its surface for weed seeds to germinate in or for moss to spread over, both of which carpet is susceptible to, causing the hoe to come into play now and then to tidy up the pile surface.

As with all gardening, each year brings its own problems, successes and failures, but taken overall the minimum dig bed system I have outlined grows vigorous, healthy, organic crops for less time and work than more conventional methods. The soil is improving steadily under this system too, becoming darker and more friable. Earthworms have become very numerous, their countless burrows and casts improving the un-dug soil structure. Soil-borne pests are decreasing with strict crop rotation.

We are still learning but one thing is already certain: minimum-dig beds can supply near self-sufficiency in quality organic vegetables the year round.

Chapter 18
The fox and the ducks

February 1991, and a spell of bitterly cold weather had lasted for several days, with snow on the ground and the river iced over. Air temperatures barely rose to freezing point around midday, and then plummeted again before nightfall. It was hard on the livestock, but we supplied extra feed to help them cope with the conditions. The wildlife was not so lucky and struggled to survive.

Snipe overwintering here were unable to probe with their long bills into soft mud along the lake or river margins and were forced to feed close to the farmyard, where a short stretch of fast-flowing mill leat remained ice-free. Normally wary birds, they tolerated our presence within a few yards during this period. With hindsight, this was a clue to the danger ahead.

At nine o-clock on a bright morning I set off on the feeding rounds, releasing the ducks from their overnight house and leading them across the yard, through the side gate to enjoy their breakfast by the mill leat. I re-crossed the yard to feed the pig, then pressed on to the field beyond with hay and water for the ewe flock. A fresh dusting of overnight snow had filled previous tracks and left everywhere gleaming white in the morning sunshine.

Cutting across behind the house with more hay for the over wintering lambs in a distant field, I glanced down at the mill leat - and stopped in my tracks. One of the Aylesbury ducks I had turned out a few minutes earlier now lay slumped against the stone wall of the mill, her pure white plumage streaked with vivid red splashes of blood. Thirty yards away at the fence bordering the river lay another, while others cowered under the branches of a fallen apple tree. As my eyes took in this unbelievable scene, they fell upon the gateway through to the adjoining meadow, and the fox standing stock still looking back at me, colours glowing against the sunlit snow. For long seconds he stared, then turned and ran off out of sight, carrying nothing in his jaws.

Dropping the hay bale, I slid down the slope, vaulted the wire fence and ran to the first bird I had seen. She was still alive, but bitten in the neck and stunned with shock. The second bird I reached was the same, but had buried her head, ostrich-like, in the snow. At the sight of me two more ducks emerged quacking from the fallen tree, again bitten in the neck, but alive. This left four more birds unaccounted for in my first frantic circuit of the paddock. Carrying the immobilised birds and gently driving the others, I returned them to the safety of the duck house and shut the door while I searched for more survivors.

Perhaps the lighter Welsh Harlequins, being better fliers, had flown over the fence onto the river in their panic to escape the predator. I moved downstream at the edge of the bank, calling quietly, and they answered from a small run of ice-free water beneath an overhanging willow. With my encouragement two birds emerged from cover, the resplendent drake with only one of his two ducks. At first glance they appeared unhurt, but of the second duck there was no immediate sign. I soon found the last Aylesbury duck by following her tracks in the snow, overprinted by fox in a dramatic record of events - down the steep bank, running faster with wings flapping, the sudden melee of the attack, the still-warm body lying crumpled nearby on the blood-flecked snow.

I persuaded the Welsh Harlequins back into the duck house to rejoin the others. Then began a long search of the surrounding area for the missing Welsh Harlequin duck, but no sign could be found of her. We never did learn her fate.

Back at the duck house I inspected each bird in turn to find that only one was beyond hope; she was mercifully dispatched. The others, although bitten, still had some use of their neck muscles and had not lost much blood. Shock was the biggest danger, so I left them alone as much as possible for the next few days in the semi-darkness of their familiar house.

For two days they languished, hardly eating or drinking, silent and subdued. On the third day I left the door of their house open for a while; on the fourth day they ventured just outside for an hour before hiding away again. But gradually they picked up from there and began to clean up their soiled feathers, taking an interest in the comings and goings around the farmyard, quacking for their twice-daily feed with enthusiasm, still a little stiff and awkward in their movements, but improving daily. Once the cold weather had passed they were free-ranging behind the mill again, looking as if nothing had ever happened to them and laying eggs as fast as ever.

Analysing the experience afterwards, we had mixed feelings. Foxes here are a part of the wildlife and the countryside, and it gives us pleasure to see them around. We had no desire for retribution. It seemed that during the bitter cold spell, hunger had forced wild animals and birds to take risks that they would not normally entertain, for while we see plenty of foxes here, they do not normally approach so close to the buildings in broad daylight. We should have anticipated the risk and taken extra care with our poultry.

In fact this is the first time that we have lost free-range poultry to the fox. We shut them away safely before dusk, let them out after breakfast, and nowadays take extra care during severe weather, keeping them indoors or within the farmyard temporarily. Plenty of people around us do lose birds to foxes, but enquiry usually reveals that they were not shut away at the right times or that the housing was not fox-proof; so often the management is at fault while the fox gets the blame.

So the next time it snows or freezes hard - watch out for your poultry.

Chapter 19
Tea with lambs

We'd been to tea with some new-found friends and had a thoroughly enjoyable time. Our respective children had played together, adults had chatted non-stop and the tea was a most delicious spread of home baking. After such a successful occasion, we were keen to return the compliment, and so arrangements were made for a Sunday afternoon during our lambing season.

Rosie was busy baking during the days leading up to this appointment, while our flock of twenty-odd ewes began lambing fairly quietly, so that by the time Sunday came, only six had produced their offspring. The day dawned dry and bright, so the heavily pregnant ewes were turned out from their overnight housing onto nearby pasture, where we could keep a close eye on them. There were no signs through the morning or after lunch. Then, when our guests arrived early in the afternoon, we set off for a stroll around a roughly circular route through the fields, to enjoy the spring-like weather, finishing up among the ewe flock once more - and there was a Jacob ewe showing a little black tail sticking out, just below her own. A breech presentation of the lamb, and she hadn't shown any of the usual early signs.

The lamb could not pass through the birth canal in this position, so we had to deal with the situation pretty quickly. We called in the whole flock and separated the ewe into a lambing pen. Our guests enjoyed this part, but they had never kept livestock themselves and were rather taken aback when I outlined what had to be done next. The head of the family volunteered to stay and help, but his wife and children paled at the prospect and beat a hasty retreat into the house.

We turned the ewe upside down, with a bale under her back for support and her back legs firmly held. I scrubbed my hands and forearms clean, applied plenty of obstetric gel lubricant and set to work, applying steady pressure to the stuck hindquarters of the lamb. At first the ewe struggled and strained against me, but gradually she relaxed and I began to make progress, gently replacing the lamb back into the womb. Now up to my elbow inside her, I could feel a mass of legs and heads - for these malpresentations seem to occur most often when more than two lambs are present.

I'd had to deal with this situation before and knew what to do. The technique is to keep hold of the lamb's tail while feeling round to one side of the hindquarters with the free fingers for a back leg. This leg is then brought gently forwards and upwards towards the birth canal. Still keeping hold of the tail, the free fingers then work round the other side of the hindquarters to locate the second back leg,

90

bringing this forwards and up also. If this sounds straightforward, believe me it isn't, not when there are twelve legs to choose from! But keeping track of the tail all the time helps to avoid the mistake of bringing the wrong leg forward. It takes care, time and patience.

Once I had the lamb correctly presented, we lowered the ewe onto her side and let her carry on with the birth as first the back legs, then tail and hindquarters appeared. At this point I withdrew the rest of the lamb swiftly, for the umbilical cord breaks whilst the head is still inside the birth canal and that first breath of life must take place in the air beyond. The lamb was alive and vigorous, and I felt both relief and satisfaction in equal measure.

With this hindrance removed, the ewe soon produced two more healthy lambs, one after the other, without further assistance. Once the messy part was over, our guests trooped back to admire the triplets, now miraculously wobbling around on unsteady legs, looking for that first drink from their mother's udder. I washed and tidied up while Rosie put the kettle on; then I thought to have a quick look at the rest of the flock.

Two more ewes had started to give birth.

Rosie made a pot of tea for our guests, slipped across to help me separate these two from the flock and into lambing pens, then dived back to finish laying the tea table. By the time she rejoined me to monitor progress, another two had started off.

Perhaps in a large flock with spacious housing and facilities, four or five ewes lambing simultaneously may present little problem. In our small flock, where housing is limited, individual animals are important and we expect to attend carefully to every lambing, five in one short spell overwhelm both our facilities and our energies. Suffice it to say that Rosie and I were kept at full stretch for some time, dealing with this unprecedented situation, whilst our guests ended up eating tea on their own at the kitchen table! We slipped into the house to make further pots of tea and to apologise profusely, for we were very embarrassed at our predicament; but to their great credit our guests laughed it all off and have remained firm friends.

We have learned our lesson from this experience and now restrict invitations during lambing time to family and friends who know just what to expect!

Chapter 20
Lesson from the past

As I write, I have in front of me a standard legal agreement defining the terms between a landowner and his tenant farmer. It spells out, among other things, that hedges and trees are to be preserved; that permanent pasture must not be ploughed up; that cropping must follow a proper rotation; that produce must be consumed on the farm or, if sold, be followed by an approved manuring programme to replace those nutrients removed. It could be an ideal model produced by the Soil Association, Friends of the Earth or the many other environmental and conservation movements of today - but in fact it is a yellowing document bearing the date 10th August 1918, and bears startling witness to the fact that sustainable organic methods were the established basis of farming until relatively recently.

Just how much agriculture has changed during less than a century is brought home by study of this document. Stripping out some of the legal verbiage, here is what it has to say on the major issues:

- *"The tenant shall not cut off any hedge without giving ten days notice to the landlord in order that he may mark for preservation such saplings or standards as he may think fit"*

Contrast this with the routine removal of hedgerows as fields have been enlarged, and the widespread use of mechanical trimming devices to which standard trees are unwanted obstacles.

- *"The tenant shall not break up any pasture or meadow land but shall manage it in every respect in a good husbandlike manner. In case of breach of this covenant, he shall pay damages to the landlord of £50 for each acre so broken"*

Considering that the annual rent at this time was around £4 per acre, the sum imposed as damages effectively prohibited any ploughing of permanent pasture. More recently we have seen vast acreages of pasture destroyed by grant-aided schemes using public money under the Common Agricultural Policy of the European Union.

- *"The tenant shall preserve all timber and timber-like trees and saplings, keep them free from injury by livestock, and shall not hang gates on, nor drive nails into them"*

This clause is intended to preserve the value of trees as usable timber in the future, when grown-over nails or gate crooks may render it useless except as firewood - and even then will blunt the axe or saw of those who follow.

- *"The tenant shall cultivate, manure and manage the farm in a proper and husbandlike*

manner on the six course system as practised in the neighbourhood .... and shall not take two corn crops without an intervening crop of turnips or similar roots . . . and shall seed out the land in its proper course with good grass seeds, to remain sown down for three years at the least"

This manner of cropping, correctly followed, ensured that the land remained in good heart and protected the landlord against the degradation of his soil by over-extractive methods.

- *"The tenant shall not mow any pasture land more than once in any year and shall manure the land mown with a sufficient and customary quantity of dung"*

It has become common practice nowadays to take two, three, and sometimes four, cuts for silage off the same field, with heavy application of artificial fertiliser between cuts.

- *"All produce grown on the farm (except threshed corn) shall be consumed thereon. If any hay or straw shall be destroyed by fire, the tenant shall bring and expend on the holding an equivalent in manure to one-third the market value of such hay or straw. In every case in which the tenant shall sell or dispose of produce in contravention of these terms, he shall give notice to the landlord in writing specifying the produce sold . . . and the provision made to return the full manurial value to the holding of such produce"*

Threshed grain was thus the only arable or root crop which could be sold off the farm, all others being recycled via livestock back onto the land so that fertility was not eroded.

Many more clauses follow in similar vein, covering every conceivable aspect of land management. Overall, the agreement clearly intends to protect the land, preserving its long-term fertility along with its hedges and timber for future generations. The approach it describes had succeeded in these objectives for a very long period of time, and so was proved beyond doubt; but over the last fifty years, most of this accepted wisdom has been cast aside as mechanisation and chemicals have replaced good husbandry. What seems to have been lost more than anything is a sense of responsibility, while in its place is a ruthless drive for ever-increasing yields, with no care for the future.

This old document once bound the tenant of our own smallholding to farm it in a sustainable fashion, for I came across it among the deeds when we purchased. We now try to follow its principles in our own management of the same land - for no other approach makes any sense to us in the long term.

Chapter 21
Open to the public

A few years ago we rented a self-catering holiday home on a small farm in a remote situation yet with a steady flow of tourists. We were eighteen months into smallholding and keen to learn. Eagerly we read the farm trail booklet that extolled the virtues of organic methods, humane husbandry, self-sufficiency and positive management for wildlife. Here were all the ideals that we ourselves were starting to practise. On arrival we found that the trail itself was no longer open to public access; instead, the pages of the booklet were displayed around a small information area. But being paying guests, our request for permission to walk around was granted, and we set off full of anticipation.

Passing through overgrazed, almost grassless pasture, we found a solitary, lonely sheep. The vegetable garden had small areas cultivated amongst an unkempt and weeded majority. The house cow looked well enough on better grazing, but the bull was confined to a walled yard that was full of sawn-off tree branches so that he had no choice but to stumble amongst them. The pig was hard to find, but through a barn cluttered with all manner of junk we could hear and smell him. At the far end of the barn we found a very small dark, dank room with one tiny window high up in the wall. The pig stood alone, knee deep in his own muck in this miserable prison.

Were these animals better off than their factory-farmed equivalents?

We had set off with high hopes of seeing the ideals expressed within the booklet put into practice, but we returned disillusioned and angry at the apparent neglect of livestock and the betrayal of principle. Enquiries revealed that the booklet had been produced several years before, in the early days of the present owners, and thus contained their initial dreams and enthusiasm that had not been sustained during the long years of reality. It had become, in fact, the worst possible advertisement for sustainable self-sufficiency.

It would be unfair to name the farm, as this took place some time ago and things may have changed by now (I sincerely hope so), but the lesson remained with us from that holiday: that if you set yourself up to preach a message, you must be seen to practise what you are preaching.

Time has passed and now our own holding is open to the public in a small way. It started with a suggestion from a nearby self-catering holiday business whose owners had become friends. They thought that their clients would jump at the chance to meet our tame livestock and to see hand spinning or natural dyeing demonstrated, and promised to point them in our direction if we would open at some pre-arranged time each week through the holiday season. We had vaguely planned to open our old water mill once it was restored to working order, but that day was a long way off.

"We can't open yet" we protested, *"we're not ready"*.

"Nonsense" said our friends *"the mill is fascinating as it stands and you can ask for donations towards the restoration costs"*.

So began our "open evenings", one each week from May to September. Posters were designed, photocopied and displayed locally at bed & breakfast or self-catering holiday places in and around the village. Some locals would turn up among the visitors, interested to see what we were up to. Attendance varied up to a maximum of forty-plus, but more typically twelve to fifteen people. The evening started off with a guided walk around the holding, meeting our free-range livestock along the way - coloured ewes and lambs that rush over to be tickled, the Tamworth sow with her piglets, ducks and their ducklings, the neighbour's heifers on summer grazing here. On the way we would pause to take in the lovely views of the river valley, look at the flower-rich meadows, the laid hedges, field corners planted with trees, the new lake and conservation area. Returning to the farmyard, we looked at the traditional stone and slate outbuildings, then the gardens for vegetables and dye plants. Up in the craft workshop over the stable, Rosie would

give a short demonstration of hand spinning or natural dyeing. Finally, I would lead a guided tour of the old mill with its surviving machinery.

All this took at least two hours and there was much more to see and do, but with the light failing and young children tired, it was all that could be covered. We made no false claims nor preached any message, just showed openly what we were learning to do. We made no charge but requested donations towards the mill restoration fund. A few home-produced items were also offered for sale.

We learned a great deal from that first season about dealing with the public, and were more adventurous the following year, opening for a full day each week. Visitors were handed a one-page leaflet bearing a map of the holding with a suggested circular walk marked out, plus a brief description of what could be seen along the way, and were left to make their own way round. We produced a twenty-page booklet for purchase by those who wanted more detailed information on the mill and our smallholding enterprise. Short talks and demonstrations were arranged at intervals through the day. We had thought that these arrangements would permit us to carry on to some extent with our normal daily work, but in practice this did not work out very well. With people arriving in family groups at odd times through the day, it proved impractical to stick to a fixed timetable of talks and we ended up dealing with each individual group as they returned to the yard from their walk around. This was actually a lot more time-consuming than doing one all-embracing evening tour. By the end of that season, we had grown tired of saying or demonstrating much the same thing several times each open day. We had given up the best part of a day's work each week, yet the total number of visitors (and therefore the donations received) had only shown a marginal increase over the previous year.

Alongside these open days ran our first school visits, as a natural development of Rosie's part-time supply teaching in a few local schools. She brought her classes here to pond-dip, to see the fleece cut from a sheep and spun into yarn, to do natural dyeing and to fire clay pots in a primitive kiln. Word spread, other teachers approached us, coaches arrived carrying up to fifty children (often the whole school here in rural Devon). These visits took up our day but were varied and enjoyable for us to plan and carry out.

At the time of writing, we are into our third season of opening to the public and have reverted back to the original "open evening" at a fixed time and day each week. More schools have booked for day visits, and other groups have approached us for day or evening bookings, such as Women's Institute, Garden Clubs, Wildlife Trust and other adult organisations.

Why do we bother? Certainly not for the money; for the donations received, although welcome, are trivial compared to the time and effort we put in. It's partly to do with sharing our good fortune at living here with others, allowing some public access in an area that lacks footpaths. It's partly to do with sharing our newfound knowledge and enthusiasm for smallholding - for many of our visitors harbour the dream of becoming smallholders themselves, one day.

Some are quite moved by their visit, some return again and become friends. Perhaps if we encourage a few others to change lifestyles, and if we also help in a small way to raise public awareness of the sustainable, organic approach to farm husbandry, then the effort of opening to the public is worthwhile.

Footnote: If you intend to open your own smallholding to the public in some way, do make sure that you are covered by adequate public liability insurance. Seek advice from your insurers before you start and give careful thought to safety on your premises. It is your responsibility, in law, to take all reasonable safety precautions.

Chapter 22
Looking Back

(The article on which this chapter is based was written in 1995)

Eight years have now passed since Rosie and I uprooted ourselves plus two young children from the "rat-race" of middle England, moving far away to a completely new lifestyle in smallholding. We look back now with astonishment at how we once lived, and at the people we used to be - for undoubtedly we have changed in many ways, as do all who return to close contact with the land. This final chapter attempts to provide some measure of how much our lives have altered, not for the sake of nostalgia, but rather to offer encouragement to those who have yet to take the plunge into smallholding.

It took four years of planning and preparation before we finally moved into our Devon smallholding. It wasn't easy to move far away from family, friends and the familiar surroundings in which we had ourselves been brought up. The "culture shock" of arriving in a small rural community was very real and it took time for us to adjust. Nevertheless, our overall feeling was one of euphoria; we had escaped from a lifestyle which no longer made any sense to us.

Our dream of a country cottage with a paddock had turned into the reality of a farmhouse, range of outbuildings with a disused water mill, and sixteen acres of permanent pasture, all of which was in need of attention. This was far more than we had intended to take on, but it was a challenge we could not resist. I had never mixed any mortar nor laid a single brick before, so there was everything to learn for the restoration and maintenance of the buildings as well as the fencing, gates and hedges for our livestock.

We initially let the grazing to a local shepherd and spent a twelve-month "apprenticeship" with his flock, working alongside him to learn the husbandry tasks around the year, before we began to acquire our own stock. Ducks and chickens came early on, sheep and pigs later as confidence grew. An old tractor was acquired, followed by a growing collection of rusting implements, which enabled us to make our own hay and bedding, to cut and harrow the pasture, and to lift and move all manner of loads around the holding. A vegetable garden was laid out and cultivated on the bed system, to yield fresh, organic produce for the kitchen all year round.

Positive action was taken to benefit wildlife alongside our domestic stock. No chemicals were used on the land, the only fertiliser being honest muck; field corners were fenced off to grow wild, or planted with native trees; a small lake was dug to extend the range of habitats available; ungrazed areas of rough grass were established for small rodents and specialised plants; hedges were laid by hand and left untrimmed to form wildlife corridors along field boundaries. Fences were put up; ditches cleaned out; blocked drains cleared; collapsed stone and turf-faced hedge banks were rebuilt; new hedges planted; gateposts set into the ground; gates made and hung. Restoration of the farmhouse was partially grant-aided thanks to the poor sanitation arrangements, so builders had to be used for this; we worked alongside them at the non-grant-aided areas, learning from them all the time. The collapsing hay barn was restored; the stable hayloft converted and fitted out as a craft workshop; livestock pens were erected; a concrete yard laid; a stone wall built edging a newly-created garden. The derelict lean-to greenhouse was demolished and rebuilt along the lines of the original. A small, damp extension of the farmhouse was stripped, re-floored, re-roofed and dry-lined to convert it into habitable and snug accommodation.

All this, and much more besides, required knowledge and skills that we did not have before. New areas of interest arose from our adopted lifestyle: friendship and cooperation with new smallholders and established farmers; stalls to sell our crafts and produce at agricultural shows; open days giving public access to our smallholding; day-workshops and evening class tuition to both children and adult groups over a range of craft and rural subjects.

Our children Katie and Martin, then aged seven and four respectively, enrolled at the village school just a few hundred yards away from our new home. We had made a point of visiting this as a part of our decision-making process, and were impressed with the commitment of the teaching staff and by the warm community atmosphere that prevailed. There were only twenty-eight pupils between the ages of rising five and eleven, so the two classes were small with all the associated benefits.

How we envied them their country childhood! This quiet rural backwater was a giant playground for inventive youngsters. There were our own fields, hedges and copses to wander at will, the natural world to discover, the river to explore. They made dens, invented games and adventures; while I provided swings and a tree house, and encouraged close contact with our livestock. Beyond our immediate boundaries they shared in the similar worlds of newfound friends, while the sea with its beaches, cliffs and rock-pools was close enough for frequent visits. As they grew older, we could safely allow them an increasing level of independence to cycle and play on their own. The combination of outdoor exercise with an organic diet of our own produce was the healthiest basis for their upbringing that we could imagine.

Rosie and I also undoubtedly benefited from the move. I became physically fitter and stronger through regular manual work; the stress of my former lifestyle quickly faded away to leave me more relaxed; while our new direction rewarded us both with a positive sense of achievement. Everything was so new, different and challenging that each day was full of interest; we loved every minute and there were few regrets.

Eight years on, we have learned so much and yet we are humbly aware of how much more there is yet to learn. There are many aspects of livestock husbandry, arable farming and horticulture which we have not even begun to experience. It seems that one lifetime will not be long enough, as it has never been for anyone. Years ago, I was puzzled by a remark in one of John Seymour's books (I forget which) wherein he qualified an incident in his own youth with the phrase "*when I was even more ignorant than I am now*". Here was a man who had spent many years living, studying and writing about rural self-sufficiency, describing himself in derogatory terms. Only now do I understand the truth and humility with which it was written.

Looking back, it seems astonishing that we could ever have been so ignorant ourselves. How could we have gone through the education system to degree level, then lived, worked and played into our late thirties without knowing how to feed, clothe and house ourselves? All that society had really taught us was the intellectual means to earn money, without which we were helpless.

Now, we produce a large proportion of our own food, including vegetables, fruit, meat and eggs. It is not a frugal existence either - there is plenty, of a quality unknown to the shopping housewife. The freshness of home produce is a major advantage, but there are others too. Varieties of vegetables or fruit can be selected for flavour rather than for appearance or shelf life, as commercial buyers demand. Traditional livestock breeds offer just the same premiums of taste and texture over the modern intensively bred hybrids. So the smallholder can produce superior quality food simply by avoiding the need to standardise or to maximise quantity. Grown organically, such food not only tastes better, it *is* better, containing no chemical residues or artificial additives, only goodness.

We do buy some foodstuffs that would be difficult or impossible to produce ourselves, including fruit from warmer climates plus some basic items like flour, milk, butter and cheese. We try to be realistic about our level of self-sufficiency; if we **had** to, we could manage without the imported fruits, but they are a welcome addition to the diet, especially in winter. Our heavy land and wet climate would make wheat-growing a struggle, but it could be done, if we **had** to; and while we have a ready supply of fresh raw milk, straight from a near-neighbour, there is little incentive for us to enter the tie of having to milk our own livestock. These are personal choices at present that may change in the future.

In our former lifestyle, I travelled to work five days a week; same journey, same traffic jams, same office; each day rather predictable, irrespective of weather or season. Colleagues little older than myself suffered illness, even death from stress-related conditions. Nowadays, I do some work virtually every day, with little difference between weekdays and the weekend or holidays. There is no travelling to and fro, apart from a short walk across the yard or maybe a ride over the fields on the tractor. Some routine jobs remain much the same, but mostly each day is different and unpredictable, the tasks changing with the weather and with the seasons. Because most of the work is enjoyable and gives satisfaction, it ceases to be a chore and the artificial divisions between work and leisure become blurred. Haymaking, for example, is hard, hot, dusty work with no certainty of success at the end - but we love it.

Now, we have the time to do more for ourselves, instead of paying others. Chimney needs sweeping? Don't ring the sweep - fetch the brushes. Slates blown off the roof - find the ladder. Concrete floor needs repair - bring out the mixer. Ewe unable to lamb - roll up your sleeves and assist. Want bacon and ham - salt down your own. Want beer - brew it. Want bread - bake it. Want firewood - cut some. There is a great deal that any able-bodied family can do for themselves, but there are limits.

Some limits are set by lack of particular skills or knowledge, others by personal choice. I tackle routine electrical wiring, for example, but will call in a professional for more intricate work; or I carry out simple maintenance on the car, but take it to the local garage for major attention. As with the food we produce, these limitations are a personal choice and could be changed, but we see nothing wrong in occasionally employing craftsmen within the local community when the need arises. For us, self-sufficiency is only practical up to a common sense limit, beyond which a struggle to achieve something without external help becomes hard to justify.

The net result of doing more for ourselves instead of paying others is twofold. Firstly, less money is needed, so less time needs to be spent earning it, thus neatly reversing the vicious circle in which modern society had previously trapped us. Secondly, it inspires self-confidence, the belief in our ability to cope. We see this quality in many of the smallholders whom we have come to know; not usually overconfidence, just an unspoken inner strength.

Our quality of life is so different here, so vastly improved from before, that it is hard to imagine now living in any other way. Of course, it is not idyllic all the time by any means. There are days when the weather is against us, when nothing seems to go right, or when our best efforts fail to achieve their purpose. As I write this, a south-westerly gale is buffeting torrential rain against the window pane, and not long ago, I was outside in full waterproofs on the evening livestock round. Feed, muck-out and bed-down the pigs; move the ewe lambs from their riverside grazing to higher ground because of flood risk; feed and shut in for the night assorted ducks, geese and chickens at various locations; carry a hay-bale through slippery mud to fill the feeding racks for the ewe flock; struggling all the time against the wind and rain to finish up cold, wet and muddy.

These conditions are accepted with a shrug, for the hardships serve to heighten appreciation of the better times, those other days when a similar round is sheer pleasure; when a sharp frost and low winter sunshine transform the familiar landscape into brilliance; or the drowsy warmth of a summer evening finds us lingering outside long after the round is finished, reluctant to move indoors after a long, hot day outside. Yes, there are times when it **is** idyllic, after all.

So now, after eight years, our lives have changed in many ways and, almost to our surprise, we find that we are no longer raw beginners. There remains so much more to learn that we know our apprenticeship will continue for a very long time to come.

Epilogue

Is there a living to be made in smallholding? This is the question we are most frequently asked; yet there is no simple answer to it. Different people have a wide range of expectations, largely influenced by their existing standards. Some strive to earn as much income as possible from a small acreage, while others concentrate on meeting their own needs to thereby reduce expenditure. We think that the endeavour to maximise income can grow into an energy-consuming business that may defeat the point of moving to the country in the first place.

Before making our own move, we came across a useful rule-of-thumb in our reading: that however self-sufficient we became, we should still expect the need to earn between one-third and one-half of our former income. This has turned out to be accurate for us.

Some level of initial capital is needed as well as income. In our case, we raised sufficient capital through the sale of our former home to purchase our smallholding outright and to finance the house improvements that were necessary. Further expenditure around the smallholding (gates, fencing, buildings, machinery, livestock) then swallowed up more of our remaining capital over the first few years, until our income rose to balance this.

There are few certainties in smallholding, but uncertainty is to be embraced as part of the attraction of this new lifestyle. Coping with uncertainty promotes a valuable sense of independence and self-confidence. Our own finances have not borne much resemblance to our initial planning, but the flexibility to recognise and respond to new opportunities has enabled us to make ends meet, so far.

In April 1994, the bi-monthly, black-and-white *Home Farm* magazine was re-launched as a glossy colour monthly that has evolved into the current format of *Country Smallholding*. Rosie began to contribute articles from that point onwards, so that either one of us would write a regular monthly feature. Over the years that followed, we covered a wide range of smallholding subjects in practical detail, always founded firmly within our own experience. Little did I realise, when that first article was published way back in 1990, that we would still be writing for the magazine all these years later! These later articles will form the basis of our second book, continuing our smallholding story while offering considerably more hard-earned experience and information as well.

Thank you for reading this book; I do hope that you have enjoyed it and perhaps learned something from it. I would value your comments and suggestions, via e-mail to ~~alan.beat@talk21.com~~ or by post to The Bridge Mill, Bridgerule, Holsworthy, Devon EX22 7EL. If you wish, you can also register to receive advance details of our second book via the same routes.

Email
alan@thebridgemill.org.uk

Visit our website:
www.thebridgemill.org.uk

The Yarner Trust is dedicated
to the ideal of living in harmony with
the environment.
To this end it offers educational courses
and practical experience in the skills of
self-reliance, organic food production and
sustainable living.

SMALLHOLDING & SELF-SUFFICIENCY
HEDGELAYING
CREATING AN ORGANIC KITCHEN GARDEN
STRAW BALE & COB BUILDING
WILLOW & HEDGEROW BASKETS
RAIN WATER HARVESTING

Just some of the courses available at
The Yarner Trust.

If you would like more information about courses
or any other aspect of our work please contact
us for more details.

The Yarner Trust, Welcombe Barton, Welcombe,
Bideford, Devon EX39 6HF
Tel: 01288 331692
enquiries@yarnertrust.co.uk
www.yarnertrust.co.uk

Essential Poultry and Smallholding Books

Starting with Chickens. Katie Thear. 96 Pages. Paperback. Well illustrated in colour. **Best selling chicken book in UK!** **£6.95**
Starting with Bantams. David Scrivener 96 Pages. Paperback. Excellent introduction with colour and mono photographs. **£7.95**

Starting with Ducks. Katie Thear. 96 Pages. Paperback. Colour and mono. Pure breeds, commercials and ornamentals. **£7.95**

Starting with Geese. Katie Thear. 96 Pages. Paperback. Colour and mono. Pure breeds, commercials and ornamentals. **£7.95**

Incubation. Katie Thear. 96 Pages. Paperback. Covers hatching and rearing of wide range of poultry and other birds. **£6.95**

Keeping Quail. Katie Thear. 96 Pages. Paperback. Excellent coverage of Coturnix, Bobwhite & Chinese Painteds. **£6.95**
Build Your Own Poultry House Plans. 6-8 hens. Step-by-step guide/Cutting list. **£2**
Starting with Pigs. Andy Case. 80 Pages. Paperback. Ideal for smallholders. **£7.95**
Starting with Sheep. Mary Castell. New colour edition! 96 Pages. Paperback. **£7.95**

Cheesemaking & Dairying. Katie Thear. 104 Pages. Paperback. Practical and comprehensive with step-by-step guidance. **£7.95**

In Preparation: *Organic Poultry - Starting with Bees - Starting with a Smallholding*

Add £1 per book for p&p. 50p for Plans. Cheques only please. (If you want Katie Thear to autograph her books, just ask).

Orders to: **Broad Leys Publishing Ltd**
1 Tenterfields, Newport, Saffron Walden, Essex CB11 3UW.
Tel/Fax: 01799 541065. E-mail: kdthear@btinternet.com

Free Poultry Helpline
at our website: www.kdthear.btinternet.co.uk